WHALE ODYSSEY

WHALE ODYSSEY

A HUMPBACK WHALE'S FIRST PERILOUS YEAR

MICHAEL BRIGHT

BOOKS

First published in Great Britain in 2008 by
JR Books, 10 Greenland Street, London NW1 0ND
www.jrbooks.com

A catalogue record for this book is available from the British Library.

ISBN 978-1-906217-17-4

10 9 8 7 6 5 4 3 2 1

Typeset by SX Composing DTP, Rayleigh, Essex
Printed by MPG Books, Bodmin, Cornwall

All photographs courtesy of Dr Dan R. Salden/Hawaii Whale Research Foundation,
© Kohola Pty Ltd and YNR Marketing

CONTENTS

Acknowledgements   vii

Introduction   1

Chapter One: The Nursery   8

Chapter Two: Night   20

Chapter Three: Trapped!   36

Chapter Four: Islands at the Edge of the World   53

Chapter Five: Alexander Archipelago   73

Chapter Six: Killers!   91

Chapter Seven: Hawaii Home   119

Postscript   131

Notes on humpback Whales   133

Appendix I: Hawaii Geology   182

Appendix II: Common Names For The Humpback
Whale   184

Appendix III: Scientific Names   187

Appendix IV: Resouces: Useful Websites   194

References   198

Index to Notes   212

ACKNOWLEDGEMENTS

It is impossible to create a story like *Whale Odyssey* without reference to the work of countless whale researchers and their enthusiastic voluntary assistants who are in the field day and night, often in a hostile ocean or on a windswept headland, when the rain is lashing or the sun baking. I would like to thank them all for amassing such a wealth of fascinating observations. Many of their published works are listed in 'References' at the end of the book, and their institute websites are listed in Appendix IV.

I would like to offer special thanks to Ross Isaacs in Queensland and Stan Esecson in California for access to still-frames from their wonderful high definition television film *Humpbacks: From Fire to Ice*. It tells the story of the first year in the life of a young humpback whale, a parallel story to that of Knucklehead except that the star of Ross and Stan's film is a young beauty – a female calf, and many of the stills are of her and her mother. The film's website is: http://www.fromfiretoice.com

Photography of whales & dolphins in Hawaiian and Alaskan waters was carried out under National Marine Fisheries Services (NMFS) permit #587-1472-00, #587-1767-00 and #587-1767-01 issued to Dr. Dan R. Salden/Hawaii Whale Research Foundation.

I would like to thank a number of researchers, cameramen and camerawomen, producers, editors and eminent scientists, some of whom I have had contact with through the film *Humpbacks: From Fire to Ice* and others through films, television and radio programmes on sharks, whales and whaling with which I have been involved in the past few years. Their research, stories and advice have been invaluable in the preparation of this book. They include: Michelle Addington, Doug Allan, Shiela Anderson, Ole Brix, Mark Carwardine, Malcolm Clark, Rob Collis, Peter Evans, Sue Flood, Ian Fergusson, John Ford, Dione Gilmore, Jonathan Gordon, Mike deGruy, Sean Hanser, David Helton, Louis Herman, Kim Holland, Martha Holmes, Bill Holshevnikoff, Jeff Kalbach, Joy Lynn, David Matilla, Naomi McIntosh, Andy Netley, Steve O'Shea, Adam Pack, Vassili Papastavrou, Roger Payne, Adam Quinn, Dan Salden, Fred Sharp, Peter Tyack, Cynthia D'Vincent and Jeff Walters. Any inaccuracies or blunders that might have crept into Knucklehead's story and in the notes on humpback whales, of course, are exclusively mine.

Thank you also to Jeremy Robson for his encouragement and faith in the idea and to senior editor Lesley Wilson for pulling the whole shebang together. And last, but no means least, thank you to Family Bright for its unwavering support.

INTRODUCTION

This is the story of the first year in the life of a humpback whale calf. He was born in waters close to the Hawaiian island of Maui and together with his mother embarked on a staggering 3,000-mile journey across the Pacific Ocean before he was no more than a few months old. The calf is called Knucklehead; at least that is the name we have given him, not a disparaging term, but a colloquial name for a humpback whale on account of the bumps on his head. Knucklehead is not a single, identifiable whale, but a composite of many whales. His story is based on actual reports from whale biologists or anecdotes from those on the sea, with a touch of artistic licence thrown in for good measure.

Humpback whales are undoubtedly charismatic animals. Who can fail to be moved by a mother gently nudging her calf or be awestruck by a 45-foot-long adult breaching, almost its entire body clear of the water? In some ways, whales are like us. They are warm-blooded mammals, they give birth, suckle their young and mothers have a strong relationship with their offspring, but at the same time they live in a world that is very different to our own.

Whales spend much of their time under the sea, so their lives are steeped in mystery. They rise regularly to the surface to breathe and some of their more spectacular behaviours are at the surface for all to see. These, however, are no more than moments in a life that can span 60, 100, or, in the case of bowhead whales, over 200 years. Scientific research at sea is expensive and extraordinarily difficult, so studies are limited. Nevertheless, scientists are finding ways and are using all manner of new techniques, from DNA analysis of tiny samples of skin to work out who is related to who, to radio-tracking by satellite, to find out where they go, when and possibly why.

The most common tool used today is photo-identification, a technique devised in 1968 by pioneer whale researcher Charles Jurasz, then with Alaska's Glacier Bay National Monument. Individual humpback whales can be recognised by their own distinctive markings. Humpbacks have the convenient habit of raising their tail flukes when they dive so if researchers follow behind them, they can photograph the underside of the flukes. Each fluke has a different pattern of black or white pigment, as well as scars and more serious injuries. It is like a fingerprint, each whale's markings unique to itself. Scientists, such as the whale biologists of the Kewalo Basin Marine Research Laboratory and the Hawaii Whale Research Foundation, keep photographic records of these flukes, so photographs of whales in Hawaii or Mexico can be compared to those, say, in Alaska or Japan. In this way, the occurrence of whales in different parts of the northern Pacific Ocean can be plotted and their likely journeys imagined.

One of the oldest photo-ID whales is NMMLID 229, thought to be a male that was first photographed by Jurasz in 1972 in Lynn Canal in southeast Alaska. It was sighted again in summer 2007, and has been photographed in Alaska or Hawaii at least once a year for 35 years.

Satellite tagging projects, like those undertaken by Oregon State University, will eventually fill in the gaps and enable scientists to track whales and trace their actual routes. It is still difficult, however, if not impossible to document the true story of a single whale, but by gathering together data and stories about humpbacks from around the world, we can begin to build a picture of what a young humpback's life might be like.

There are a few celebrity whales that have held people's imagination and dominated the headlines. There is Migaloo, a famous white humpback that joins the great whale migration along the east coast of Australia, and there is a conventionally coloured Mister Splashy-Pants, that was satellite tagged by Greenpeace in the southern Pacific. Newspapers worldwide drew readers' attention to the wildly erratic Humphrey. He pitched up twice in San Francisco Bay and hit the headlines worldwide. Similarly, Dawn and Delta, a mother-and-calf duo, entered the Bay and their exploits drew thousands of spectators to the waterside. Each of these whales were under scrutiny for days, even weeks, but what they actually do with the rest of their time and where they actually go when they leave the glare of the publicity is far from clear.

That whales are with us at all is something of a miracle. When not on migration, humpbacks favour inshore waters and shallow banks, which made them vulnerable to hunting by coastal peoples. At first this was sustainable, but from the 1800s, when whale oil was as valuable as petroleum is today, commercial whaling all but annihilated the world's population of humpbacks, along with most other species of whales. The pre-whaling stock of an estimated 15,000 whales in the North Pacific was reduced to fewer than a thousand – 7 per cent of the original population.

The sorry picture was repeating itself around the world. At Twofold Bay, New South Wales, Australia, whale was even pitted against whale. One of the humpback's natural predators is the killer whale or orca. Local pods would herd the humpback whales into the bay where whalers were waiting to kill them. The killers were rewarded with their part of the prize, usually the whale's tongue and lips. The skeleton of the largest of the killer pod, Old Tom, can be seen at Eden Killer Whale Museum. This hunt, however, was relatively small. The Davidson family, who led the hunt, took no more than eight whales a year, what the killer whales would take naturally.

Elsewhere it was far worse. In the southern hemisphere, Dutch, British, US, Norwegian and Japanese whaling ships decimated all species of whales, including humpbacks on their Antarctic feeding grounds. And the wholesale slaughter continued until 1948, when the International Whaling Commission was formed and the whale harvest was supposedly regulated. The killing continued apace. Between 1950 and 1962, for example, whaling stations on the east coast of Australia killed 12,500 humpbacks, a much faster rate than they could reproduce. During the 20th century alone, records show that worldwide 250,000 humpback whales were killed. The real figure is probably higher. One nation, which continued to hunt humpbacks after an agreed moratorium on catching the species, deliberately under-recorded its catch, reporting 2,280 kills when the true number was probably closer to 48,000.

In 1963, the killing of humpbacks in the Antarctic was banned, followed by a worldwide ban in 1966. Since 1986, all whales, including humpbacks, have been protected by an agreed international moratorium on whaling, although not all nations are playing by the rules. A few ignore the ban and continue to hunt mainly the smallest baleen whales – minke whales, while others exploit a loophole in the treaty that allows nations to hunt whales for 'scientific' purposes. At one stage recently, there was even a plan to include humpbacks in the scientific catch, but international opinion held sway.

It is thought that more than 64,000 humpbacks live in the

world's oceans today (according to population estimates from 1992–3 in the western North Atlantic, 1997–8 in the southern hemisphere south of 60° South, and 2007 in the North Pacific; source: International Whaling Commission – although North Pacific estimates are higher than expected so the world population might now be higher), but they are far from safe. Our increasingly crowded world has extended into the sea, where entanglement in fishing gear, collisions with ships, unregulated whale-watching, chemical pollution, and noise pollution from ships, military sonar, and seismic exploration are detrimental to whales.

Some whales show wounds where propellers have cut deep into their flesh or sliced off dorsal fins, and many whales are washed ashore with obvious signs of an impact with a large object, such as a ship. Whales sometimes swim vast distances, even when weighed down by trailing fishing gear. In February 2006, a 45-foot-long male humpback turned up in Hawaii with heavy-gauge fishing lines through its mouth and wrapped around its body. Two heavy-duty buoys were also attached. Local marine mammal response managers eventually freed the whale, and took the buoys away for identification. It turned out they had been on king crab gear set in Alaska. The whale, wrapped in rope, had towed them at least 2,500 miles from Alaska to Hawaii!

Similarly, but on a smaller scale, in February 2005 a 23-foot-long humpback was freed from a crab pot and buoy in Penrhyn Bay, off the North Wales coast. The gear originated from County Donegal in northwest Ireland. The whale was freed successfully. In July 2004, a humpback yearling near Perth, Western Australia, dragged crayfishing pots and floats for 370 miles. It came into shallow water to avoid attacks by great white sharks, and was very tired and swimming slowly by the time the local authorities found it and freed it. Another whale that was entangled in June 2002 was not so lucky. Sharks chewed off most of its right pectoral fin. In July 2001, eight great white sharks attacked a young humpback caught in fishing gear at the head of the Great Australian Bight. It did not survive.

All this, plus the anecdotes and published scientific accounts, are weaved into Knucklehead's story, which attempts to give a feel for what life is like for a humpback whale. Anthropomorphism is inevitable in such an endeavour, but try not to let that detract from the underlying adventure and the down-to-earth biology. 'Notes on Humpback Whales' at the end of the book summarises much of what is known about the species, the results of many long hours of painstaking fieldwork and meticulous analysis by dedicated researchers worldwide who are piecing together the actual story of humpback whales. Their work and many of the sources for Knucklehead's story are reflected in the list of 'References' at the end of the book.

The origin of the name 'humpback' is obscure. Some believe it refers to the shape of the base of the dorsal fin, others say it is on account of the whale's rounded back when diving. In *Moby Dick*, Herman Melville described the humpback as the 'most gamesome and light-hearted of all the whales'; no doubt reference to the extraordinary way its leaps clear of the water and splashes with its flippers, chin and tail.

They are, indeed, remarkable animals. Recordings of their songs, made by Roger Payne and Scott McVay in the 1970s, featured humpbacks that sang their eerie and hypnotic songs around the mid-Atlantic island of Bermuda. They captured the public's imagination, and helped bring attention to the plight of whales all over the world. Ten-and-a-half-million flexi-discs containing some of the recordings were issued along with a special edition of the *National Geographic* magazine, the largest single pressing of any record in history. Those same recordings also featured in the movie *Star Trek IV: The Voyage Home* (1986), and have been launched into space on gold discs carried aboard the two *Voyager* spacecraft, which are on their way out of our solar system and into the void of outer space.

In our story, we are very much down on Earth. We follow our hypothetical mother and calf on their seasonal journey from Hawaii's active volcanic islands and warm seas to the majesty of southeast Alaska's mountains and glaciers, a chilly world where icebergs litter the cold but productive waters. It is a journey from fire to ice and back again, during which the young whale has just one year to find out how to survive – 12 months to learn the way of whales.

CHAPTER ONE:
THE NURSERY

It happened under a full moon one night in mid-February: a baby was born. At 16 feet long and weighing close to a couple of tons, this was no ordinary baby – this was a whale…a humpback whale. The birth was private. No human had ever witnessed such an event, and this night was no exception. Enveloped in a warm subtropical sea, he arrived probably tail first and was nudged gently to the surface by his mother to take his very first breath. He flailed about at the surface, all tail flukes and flippers, an awkward baby, but within half an hour he was swimming around his mother's enormous bulk, a fully coordinated humpback.

With the first streaks of dawn lightening the eastern sky, his mother stopped and listened. She moved slowly in a large circle, aware that they were no longer alone. Shadows had gathered in the gloom of dark blue. The baby's arrival had attracted more than admiring glances. Blood and other body fluids floated away on the current, an irresistible odour that had already permeated the ocean for a mile downstream. The shadows were sharks – tiger sharks – the ocean's garbage collectors. They ate just about anything that was edible, their jaws lined with row upon replaceable row of razor-sharp teeth – a living chainsaw. They could slice through flesh, sinew and bone as if it were no more substantial than butter.

Detecting at first just a few molecules of the smell, they had followed the odour trail back to its source. They moved silently and deliberately, their bodies the epitome of power. Slow, almost languid, sweeps of the tail pushed them forward as they criss-crossed the widening corridor of enticing smells, heading against the current towards the area of greatest concentration – to where the whale mother had given birth.

They circled, surprisingly unsure of what to do next. The mother whale instinctively moved her body to protect her newborn baby. He nestled under her chin. One strike from her formidable tail could have staved in even a tiger shark's body, but such a prospect did not dissuade these wolves of the sea. There were three: two well over 15 feet long, and one somewhat smaller. The tiger stripes on the larger sharks were just about visible on the dark brown-grey of their bodies. These were older, wiser tigers. They tightened their circle. The whales remained motionless lest it provoked an attack.

Suddenly, one of the sharks lunged forward, powered through the water and grabbed a slice of afterbirth. Its move set off the other two. They rushed, almost collided, the smaller shark giving way to the bigger. It was rammed in the gills for its trouble, but managed to escape more serious injury. The larger shark turned, took the remaining whale placenta and made off. Mother and calf slipped away; her giant baby was at risk from the moment he was born.

This perilous and somewhat lively whale nursery was in shallow waters off Maui, one of Hawaii's many islands. It was in the middle of the Pacific Ocean, thousands of miles from any mainland, one of the remotest places on the planet; a hotspot on the Earth's surface where molten magma oozed from cracks in its crust to form a volcanic island chain that was the battleground between earth, fire and water.

Hawaiian mythology told a different tale. It was written that the demigod Maui went fishing with his brothers and when he cast a fishhook into the water he pulled and pulled, and out of the ocean came Hawaii. It was just the way sailors have always discovered islands: when sailing towards the horizon, they see them emerge almost magically from out of the sea.

People came here from the west. Guided by the stars, they ventured out from Asia – the so-called 'people of the sea'. They went from island to island in ocean-going, outrigger canoes – the Hokulea, journeying through the South Pacific, some settling, others moving on until they reached French Polynesia and Easter Island and then ran out of land. The legendary Polynesian adventurer Hawai-i-Loa turned to the north and found a paradise on Earth.

Maui is in the east of the archipelago, one of the taller, younger islands. A great valley separates its precipitous, green-carpeted, twin volcanic peaks and the island itself is edged in broad swathes of red, black and white sand beaches. Deeply incised valleys and steep-sided ravines carve into the mountains, and high waterfalls cascade over sheer dark rock walls, plunging into deep, clear pools.

For those ancient mariners, the ocean swells and pounding surf made this a hazardous landing place, but for a newly born humpback whale, the Au'au Channel between the islands of Maui and Lana'i is a safe haven, a shelter from the kona storms that can last from many hours to several days.

At one time, though, it was not so peaceful. In the mid-19th century, whalers set sail in open boats to take the animals that they felt were rightfully theirs. They pursued the calves with cold, iron harpoons, killing them first in order to bring in their mothers, with all their meat and blubber...but most of that is long gone. The last of the whalers died peacefully in his sleep.

In more recent times, as many as 4,000 to 5,000 humpback

whales returned here each northern winter and were not harmed. It was a national marine sanctuary set aside especially for whales. No one knew when whales first came, but now they arrived each November. Mothers came to give birth in the warm, subtropical waters or abandoned growing delinquents, and rowdy bulls came to charge down a mate. It was the biggest congregation of its kind in the Pacific, two-thirds of the entire northern Pacific population.

Unaware of his contribution to world-beating statistics, Knucklehead – for that was the name watching scientists had given him on this bright February morning – was content to wallow. As the sun rose at heaven's eastern gate, he stayed close to his mother, playing. He balanced on her snout and squirmed over and under her long flippers, sinking from time to time below her enormous bulk to take milk. It was thick like cottage cheese, pink and rich in the fats and the other good things that a growing calf needs to stay alive. He was born with just enough blubber to buffer the shock of sliding from an insulated womb to cooler Hawaiian waters, but he had to gain weight…and fast; and while *he* put on 100 pounds and grew an inch longer each day, his mother grew slimmer.

During the course of that winter, she lost a third of her weight, for she was on a self-imposed diet. Throughout her time in the subtropics she did not feed. There was food there all right – the sharks, dolphins and billfish found it – but in these subtropical seas it was patchy and predators had to swim fast to catch it; and this was the snag – humpback whales were not built for the chase. The food was not concentrated enough in one place for an enormous whale. It would not have been worth her while to use up her precious energy to collect it. To find food in such abundance she would have to go elsewhere; but for the moment she had a calf to bring up.

She had carried him for almost 12 long months, and now she

watched his every move. As she rested under the surface, he tucked back under her chin. He visited the surface often, every four or five minutes, to breathe; then he circled and dived back to his place under her body. He could not hold his breath for as long as his mother. She surfaced every 10 minutes or so. They touched frequently, her gentle reassuring nudges an encouragement for the baby whale to watch and learn. School was open, and on the timetable that day was 'how to make yourself known'. His mother showed him how it was done. She dived below and then raced back to the surface, leaving the water at speed and at such an angle, almost all of her body was clear of the water as she twisted in mid-air and landed on her side in an incredible fountain of spray.

Why she should breach in this way was unknown. Maybe it was a way to keep in touch, or maybe just fun, but the impact of whale on water must have created a deep boom that carried for miles below the sea. It told the neighbours that Knucklehead's mother was right there and at home, and it must have been important to her or she would not have bothered to use all that energy to leap clear of the water…but school was in session and she was the teacher. It was time for her calf to try, and try as he might he could barely lift his head clear, let alone breach. He was all uncoordinated – he could not get the height, but he tried hard…time and time *and* time again, and slowly his leaps became more definite and his splashes were bigger and louder – he was having his first long distance call with a distant cousin.

With his first lesson at first grade completed, Knucklehead raised his tail to dive below and…click!

He waved his flipper in the air…click!

He raised his head above the surface to find out what went click…click!

Rolling gently not far away was a small boat filled with

people, not tourists but whale biologists and they were all taking pictures of the young whale. Knucklehead had just been registered in the latest photo-identification catalogue. He was a celebrity for a day, the focus of all their attention, the new boy on the block.

He was grey all over when he was born, but as he grew he was becoming darker above and paler below, a kind of camouflage shared by many sea creatures, the dark back blending in with the deep sea when viewed from above, and the pale underside matching the brightness of the sky when seen from below. More significantly, the colour of his flippers and tail flukes was not uniform. The patchy black-and-white patterns were quite distinct and unique to him. In humpback society, no two flukes are alike – like human fingerprints. Some are mostly black, others mostly white and many more are in between. It was the way scientists could identify him at the surface and track him wherever he went and whatever he did. For the moment, they just watched.

Just then, another mother and her newborn swam by. Mothers with calves tended to avoid each other around the islands, but these two families had chanced upon each other. The two parents were clearly uncomfortable with being in such close proximity. They avoided each other's gaze, and swam slowly, almost aloofly, apart, but the youngsters were far more inquisitive. The new arrival edged towards Knucklehead and they touched briefly. The visitor was a young female. She had been born not that long ago, and was somewhat awkward too. Her long gangly flippers were pure white, and as she swam away to catch up her mother, they could be seen in the gloom, long after the rest of her body had merged with the deep blue.

Then, Knucklehead's mother was suddenly alert. The two whales were aware of even more whales nearby. They had strayed into a zone that was dangerous for baby whales. In these waters, those whales not giving birth were here to find a mate, and courtship for humpbacks was an extremely boisterous, even violent affair. Inadvertently, Knucklehead's mother had led him into a gigantic underwater arena, several miles across where the principle performers were 45- ton humpback bulls that powered through the water at 10 to 20 miles per hour…and centre of their attention for the moment was Knucklehead's mother.

The bulls moved towards her, slowly at first, each jostling for prime position next to her…this was a very dangerous place for a calf to be. He could be crushed and killed if he was caught up in a fight. After much pushing and shoving, one large male made his move and in a burst of bubbles from the blowhole on the top of his head declared himself her principle suitor or 'primary escort', as the scientists described him. The other males jostled him, but his exaggerated head movements and blocking behaviour shut them out. With a burst of speed, one of these other young pretenders – known as 'secondary escorts' by the watching scientists – pushed down on his head, but a burst of bubbles, this time from his mouth and not the blowhole, saw him off. Blowing this kind of bubble cloud was a dangerous thing for a whale to do. He had pushed a flap at the back of his throat against the roof of his mouth to form a tube from the voice box to the mouth. He then shunted air directly out through his baleen plates. If the whale failed to prevent seawater flowing back, he could drown. It was a desperate manoeuvre but it worked. The secondary escort dropped back.

The primary escort swam alongside Knucklehead's mother, calling all the while in low-pitched snorts and moans. She, in turn, put herself between the fighting bulls and her calf, keeping him close to the surface and out of harm's way. But his mother was not yet ready for mating. She would not be ready for at least another year, so she tried to shake off the over-enthusiastic males and protect her calf. She made a run for it, guiding

Knucklehead back into shallower water. The raucous group was so wrapped up in its brawling, they almost missed the fact that she and her calf were fleeing. They struggled to keep up and continued to joust well into the afternoon. Eventually, the fighting stopped and the group broke up, each whale going its separate way.

The sun had climbed high into a cloudless sky, and the sea was not quite a millpond but as close as the Pacific ever gets to one; just the slow roll of the ocean swell caused seagulls sitting on the surface to be on a crest one minute and in a trough the next. Fishing boats rocked gently at anchor, and a sailboat searched unsuccessfully for a morsel of wind, its sails flapping loosely in what was left of a breeze. It was midday, and a lazy day.

Some of the whales just hung in the water about 30 feet down, barely moving. They held their breath not for minutes like the active whales, but for a half-an-hour or more. Their behaviour, or lack of it, led scientists to call them 'breath-holders'. They drifted in the ocean current. Others remained motionless, and then they did the most extraordinary thing… they started to sing, their long sonorous moans and high frequency yelps filling the ocean with sound.

Knucklehead not only heard the songs but also felt them… the lowest notes were so loud and carried so far underwater that they reverberated through his entire body. One day, he will be a singer, just like them…but for now he 'talked' to his mother, not only with occasional grunts and burps that the listening scientists could detect, but also many other sounds at frequencies way below what they could hear.

Then, he picked up new sounds, barely discernible at first, but these were most definitely not from other humpback whales. The sounds gradually became louder as the source came closer, and there, out of the blue appeared a pod of false killer whales. They chattered noisily. The very highest frequency sounds were

15

used not to talk to each other, but either to find their way in the sea or, more ominously, to search for food. False killers are one of the top predators around the islands. They eat mainly fish, but a large group working together can be quite capable of running down and killing a baby whale, and occasionally they take a fancy to meat.

As the group drew closer, Knucklehead's mother again placed her body between the potential danger and her calf. He took his usual station above and to the right of her blowhole. They were ready to repel an attack, but no attack came. The false killers were not interested in Knucklehead. There was a school of mahi-mahi or dolphin fish working along a current line near the surface, and the false killers corralled and captured them with consummate ease. They sprayed the ocean with echolocation sounds, and the fish appeared disorientated and debilitated. They did not eat the fish immediately though. They appeared to be playing, showing a new, social dimension to their behaviour. They were passing the food around, and some of the recipients were youngsters. Just as a cheetah mother offers her cubs a live gazelle foal to catch in order to practise killing, these false killer calves were given a live but injured fish so they could learn how to kill.

Two of them appeared to be harassing the baby whale. Had they changed their tactic and were hunting for meat after all? No. These two characters were not false killers at all, but two from a mixed group of spotted and spinner dolphins. They had been picking up scraps from the false killer whale's table but now they had found something different to amuse them. Their interest in baby whales was not to hunt them but to ride with them. Survival school was out; it was playtime. The dolphins twisted and turned, riding the pressure wave immediately in front of the two large whales. Like excited children, they emitted a barrage of high-pitched sounds – whistles, clicks, burps and raspberries or 'Bronx cheers'. Many of the sounds were being used for echolocation, others a lively conversation between members of the group.

The sounds were produced in a complicated plumbing system just below their blowhole, and focused into a concentrated beam that was emitted through their shiny, bulbous forehead. The returning echoes were picked up in the lower jaw of all places, not the ear, from which tiny electrical signals carried the information via nerves to the brain. It was an extraordinarily sophisticated system, the result of millions of years of evolution. Like the false killers, it enabled the dolphins not only to avoid obstacles in the water or on the seabed, but also to find their prey. Some scientists believe that the beam of sound is so powerful it could be used to incapacitate small fish, making them easier to catch. Whatever the function, the dolphins had a dangerous weapon in their heads, and they used it wisely, even switching it off when another dolphin crossed in front of them. Believe it or not, they were showing echolocation manners.

Both Knucklehead and his mother joined in the fun. He lay across her back and as she surfaced he slid back down into the water. A piece of seaweed became a toy. He draped it over his snout, then his tail. He surfaced, lost it in the wash and then found it again floating at the surface. A dolphin joined in, letting the frond pass gently over its flipper before grabbing it in its mouth and racing to the surface before any of the others could take it. As Knucklehead wallowed and rolled in the water, the dolphins leapt over and around him, swimming rapidly back and forth, twisting and turning like demented terriers.

They whistled constantly, each dolphin with its own particular signature tune. It was easy to spot who was whistling at any one time for they emitted a thin stream of bubbles from their blowhole. Just then, a new spotted dolphin arrived to join the group. As he approached, he whistled his signature repeatedly until others copied him, and only then was he accepted into the group and was able to join in the conversation with a very different repertoire of whistles and clicks.

Young dolphins in the group, like Knucklehead, remained close to their mothers. Mother and offspring touched frequently, and when a young delinquent strayed too far, its mother thwacked it with her tail, and then brushed it with her flippers – a harsh rebuke followed by gentle reassurance. Young dolphins are vulnerable to shark attacks should they separate from the adult, and those waters were swimming with sharks.

The boisterous play stopped abruptly. The dolphins became agitated and swam more closely together. Other dolphin shapes appeared, larger animals altogether, and they made straight for Knucklehead and his mother. They were a couple of male bottlenose dolphins, the bullyboys of the dolphin world, and they were there to have some of their own brand of fun. They raced past the two whales and tore into the group of smaller dolphins, singling out an adolescent male. They chased and butted it brutally, abusing it mercilessly.

The spotted dolphins regrouped, and went on the offensive. A gang of them, working together, confronted the bottlenose bullies with open mouth threat displays and loud piercing squawks, and then chased them, ramming them with their snouts. The intruders swam off nonchalantly, as if troubled by nothing more than pesky flies; but the spotted dolphins had won the day. They were gone in a flash of flippers and flukes, and Knucklehead and his mother were suddenly alone.

His mother stopped momentarily in the water. It was time to rest, and if her calf would allow her, to sleep...well, at least doze, for she had to think when to breathe, something she had to do every 20 to 30 minutes, and 45 minutes at the very most. If she slept deeply like we do, she would drown. So, part of her brain was asleep and the other part was 'awake'. In this way, it not only checked on the next time she had to visit the surface and breathe, but also kept an eye out for predators and any other dangers.

Her eyes were small, set on either side of her head. 'Is it not curious,' wrote Herman Melville in *Moby Dick*, 'that so vast a being as the whale should see the world through so small an eye?' Curious it may have been, but with her tiny eyes she could see quite well underwater, up to 400 feet in the crystal-clear waters of Hawaii; but she had blind spots.

'Now, from this peculiar sideway position of the whale's eyes,' observed Melville, 'it is plain that he can never see an object which is exactly ahead, no more than he can one exactly astern'. It was a design fault, but not a serious one, for Knucklehead's mother relied more on sound than sight.

She also could not distinguish colours for she had only green cones and not blue ones in the retina of her eyes, and both are necessary to perceive colours. Her world was entirely black-and-white.

The two whales catnapped, an early afternoon siesta, keeping a watchful eye and an alert ear for anything untoward. They took a breath every two or three minutes. Knucklehead lay close to his mother's snout, just to make sure. His mother remained motion-less, like a log, with only her blowhole exposed occasionally at the surface, until, with a jolt, she awoke from her half sleep and slowly moved away, her offspring sticking close to her, like glue.

The sky above turned golden, then red, distant clouds dark against a sun setting in heaven's western gate. Knucklehead had been nearly crushed by humpback bulls, run down by false killer whales, and he had played with dolphins and learned how to breach, yet he was barely a day old. What a day it had been; but now came his first night, and with the darkness came real dangers.

19

CHAPTER TWO:

NIGHT

The two whales swam slowly across the Kalohi Channel along the southern shores of neighbouring Molokai towards the shallow Penguin Banks. While the near-shore waters south of Maui drop to 300 feet, the sandy sea floor of the bank is little more than 200 feet from the surface. It was a good place to spend the night.

In the eerie twilight, a flock of petrels began to twist erratically, darting and gliding, then swooping down on the water to join a scattered group of shearwaters that had begun feeding on small squid that had come to the ocean surface. Beneath them, the two whales passed slowly over a coral reef as a school of skipjack swam along its edge. The big fish were alert for smaller fish that they might catch, yet vigilant for even larger fish that might be hunting them. As if on cue, a school of menacing grey reef sharks eased their way along the drop-off into deep water where there were swarms of jellyfish, their gently pulsating half-moon bells reflecting the last vestiges of light from a sun that was already lost over the horizon.

As Knucklehead and his mother brushed the reef edge, a large shark with huge eyes suddenly appeared, but it was the unusually long scythe-shaped tail that was strange. It was all of seven feet long. The shark swam this way and that, darting in and around a school of small fishes, seeming to herd them using its tail like a stockman might use a whip. Then, with a sudden thrashing of the tail, a handful of fish were hit and lay limp in the water. The shark circled slowly, and gathered them up at leisure. With a sweep of its tail, it disappeared into the night – an unexpected encounter with a big-eyed thresher shark from the deep.

The coral reef itself was like an underwater city. Brain and pillar corals, resembling high-rise blocks, were separated by avenues paved with coral sand. Leaf-like branching cauliflower coral dominated the coral flats, colouring them dull brown and pink in the fading light. On the seaward side, orange sea fans, sea whips and sea plumes protruded from the background of finger corals. Sea urchins burrowed into the coral blocks, while black and speckled brown sea cucumbers lolled about on the sand, feather-duster worms burrowed into the coral debris, and Christmas-tree worms protruded from their tubes on the reef like miniature, fully decorated Christmas trees.

In the convoluted shallows, a green turtle was wedged beneath an overhanging coral buttress. It was holding its breath, apparently fast asleep. A puffer fish used the scales on its belly to stick to the reef wall, like Velcro, and a triggerfish jammed itself into a crack, erecting a spine on its back to lock it in place. A parrotfish hid under a coral ledge, wrapped in a mucous sleeping bag that kept its odour in and predators out. An untidy group of wrasse were the last to turn in. Squirming under the sand, eventually their eyes stopped moving and their brains shut down. It was time for the night shift to replace the day shift.

Already white-tip reef sharks were skimming the corals, searching for any telltale signs of their nocturnal feast. Later in the night they would hunt in the pitch darkness, relying on a battery of senses not only to track down their prey but also to avoid the razor-sharp coral heads. They used their wedge-shaped heads to bulldoze into cracks and crevices, following closely the giveaway odour of something edible inside. Pursued by the sharks, the orange shapes of nocturnal soldierfish and squirrelfish flashed through cracks in the corals. A long and slender moray eel squirmed from its daytime lair. It pushed and probed, driving fish from their refuges right into the paths of the feeding sharks. Like some scene from a science fiction movie the eel grabbed a victim in its powerful jaws and then grabbed it again with a second set of jaws that moved forward from its throat. Its prey was dragged in with no chance to escape.

Even the coral itself had suddenly come to life. Hawaii's fringing reefs are young compared to reefs in other parts of the world, yet myriad copepods, mysid shrimps, polychaetes, and fish larvae drifted up from their daytime hiding places, and the tentacles of countless coral polyps pushed out like flowers from their calcareous cases, waving and pulsating in a bioluminescent light show as they extracted these tiny organisms from the water. A brightly coloured sea slug, its vivid coat a warning that it is poisonous to eat, grazed on algae, while an octopus left its lair, crawled across the reef, and used its entire body to envelop a crab, biting into its shell with its vicious parrot-like beak.

Protruding like pencils from the sand at the edge of the reef was a group of garden eels. They quickly withdrew into their burrows as the whales' shadows passed over them. In the water column, a squadron of enormous manta rays one behind the other slowly flopped into view. Like huge aircraft, dark on top and white below, each was close to 20 feet across. They were here to feed, not by chasing down small fish like the sharks, but to sift plankton in the water. Propelled by their great wing-like pectoral fins, they swam in huge loops, concentrating the tiny organisms by somersaulting continuously, the devil-like horns on either side of their head guiding miniscule shrimp-like creatures into their broad letter-box-shaped mouths. They glided down with their mouths agape, turned and came around to start the run again. It was all so much for a baby whale to take in.

Knucklehead shook. He felt a sting on his belly, as if something had pinched the skin; then, there was another. The baby whale shuddered and swam closer to his mother. This was most definitely uncomfortable. The pinching stopped, but on his side there were two perfectly round holes dug out of his skin and blubber. They were bleeding, but it was not serious. It would stop soon. The culprits swam rapidly away into the darkness. They were tiny sharks – cookie-cutter sharks – small deep-sea sharks that had come up from the depths of the Pacific Ocean during the night. They were just another of the many species of deep-sea creatures making the daily vertical migration. The soft blubber of the baby whale had been too much to resist. The sharks had latched onto the skin with their sucker-like lips and enormous teeth, the largest teeth to body size of any known shark, and then used the forward motion of the whale to help twist off a circular wedge of skin and blubber. It was all over in seconds. By the time the whale had noticed, the sharks had long gone, looking for another hapless target. Knucklehead will bear the tiny scars for the rest of his life.

Just then a huge dark shape loomed out of the gloom and stopped just short of the two whales. It moaned quietly, came close but not too close. It was a bull humpback. He hovered a few yards from the young calf and his mother, not menacing but reassuring. He would be the pair's escort for the night, not for any selfless motive, but with the expectation of a pairing at sunrise. Tomorrow was already shaping up to be a very lively day indeed.

* * *

The sun eased itself from a calm subtropical sea and, as far as the eye could see, the misty blows of dozens of whales hung in the clear air of dawn. The deep-sea creatures had long gone, sinking back to their twilight zone a thousand feet below, a second marathon in 24 hours – the largest migration of animals on Earth. A distant splash and a fountain of spray betrayed a humpback breaching. A gaggle of visiting laughing gulls squabbled for scraps of food, while squadrons of resident brown boobies skimmed the waves and then climbed, momentarily stalled, and plunged headlong into a shoal of fish hidden below the surface. They were flying fish, and they were being pursued by a flock of birds from above as well as a school of yellowfin tuna from below. The tuna pushed the fish to the surface and, every now and again, one leapt clear of the water, spreading its pectoral fins and rapidly sculling its tail to propel it 100 yards or more across the surface before disappearing below once more. Closer to shore, terns and noddies dived on tiny bait fish, and white-tailed tropicbirds soared along nearby cliffs, their vivid white bodies edged in black and trailing two long, streaming tail feathers. They were heading out to sea for a day's fishing.

In the sea, a disorderly shoal of yellow tang twisted over the reef, while a belligerent, stubby-nosed, brightly striped rectangular triggerfish, unaware of its excessively long, tongue-twisting local name – humuhumu-nukunuku-apuaa – busied itself amongst the coral heads. A pair of hermit crabs fought over the occupancy of a shell, and a camouflaged scorpionfish sat on a rock for all to see, yet it had all but disappeared. Schools of black-tailed wrasse cruised by, following the green sea turtle that had been evicted from its night-time refuge by a returning moray eel. The day shift was back, and the inshore waters brimmed with spectacular underwater life.

Suddenly, Knucklehead's mother felt a sting in her back; no more than a pinprick but she felt it all the same. She dived gently and shallow, just skimming the underside of the sea's surface. The whine of an outboard motor and a grey fast-moving shape alongside betrayed the presence of scientists in an RIB (rigid inflatable boat). They had fired a small dart from a crossbow and, unknowingly, she had given a sample of her skin and blubber. Soon, her innermost secrets – the blueprint that made her almost 40 years ago – would be laid bare and her closest relatives revealed. For now, however, what she, her calf and her escort had failed to notice was another bull humpback heading straight towards them.

It passed them without a second glance. Another female and escort a half-a-mile further on had attracted his attention. Watching scientists recognised the female; she was the one with the turned-down tips to her flukes. Somehow, the bull had spotted her from nearly a mile away and was ploughing through the water at breakneck speed to get to her. He arrived like an express train, prompting the primary escort to slew almost sideways into him. The primary escort twisted about with remarkable agility for such a bulky creature and let loose a burst of bubbles. The interloper responded by ramming him, the sharp barnacles on the tip of his snout drawing blood.

By now, the three whales had picked up speed and were setting off across the ocean. More whales joined – eight, nine, ten – some of them little more than juveniles, but they were here to learn the hard way – to learn how to fight. Suddenly the primary escort rose up vertically, almost half of his body out of the water and his long flippers held out to either side like a giant crucifix. It was a 'crucifix block', aimed at stopping one of the speeding males from getting close to the female. Another raised his tail, causing his head to dip violently – a 'peduncle throw' (referring to the tail stock packed with muscles that power the tail), forcing the whale immediately behind to dive and avoid a collision.

Three young bulls in line abreast planed across the surface to join the fight. Seawater spewed from their half-open mouths and the air rushed through their blowholes, creating a frightening whistle-like roar. Another bull was raised above the surface as the larger one lifted him from underneath; then his neighbour slammed him from the side. They swerved just in time to avoid the boat filled with scientists, although a sweep of one of their tails almost capsized the RIB and the spray drenched all those on board. It was a lucky escape. Battling humpback bulls are not careful about who or what they ram when engaged in a courtship fight.

The female escaped the mêlée by moved into very shallow water, brushing the bottom with her huge, white pectoral fins and squirming past coral heads that grew from a depth of 30 feet to within a hairsbreadth of the surface. The males pealed off, ceased their fighting and slipped quietly away to find a receptive female. The scientists in the RIB, however, did not follow. They had other concerns. A radio message revealed that just before dawn a small freighter had gone aground on a nearby reef. It was suspected of running illegal drugs and was being chased by the coastguard when it hit a coral head. Now, it was haemorrhaging diesel oil from a gash in its hull and, as the wind was getting up, the slick was beginning to spread. The surface had darkened, and already several seabirds were covered in oil. The boat raced to the scene.

Knucklehead and his mother were swimming unknowingly towards the slick. They had to be stopped. The boat tried to intercept them, attempting to change their track before the pair entered the contaminated area…but nothing less than a big ship was likely to stop a humpback mother with determination. She ploughed on, the scientists becoming ever more concerned. Then, she pushed down her nose and lifted her tail flukes clear of the water and she dived down into a deepwater channel.

Knucklehead followed as best as he could. What seemed like an age passed, and then they resurfaced on the far side of the slick. The scientists breathed a sigh of relief. The two whales had missed the oil.

Below the waves, the underwater community was oblivious to the drama above. A group of parrotfish, fresh from their night-time slumbers, were doing their best to demolish the reef. Nibbling the coral with their hard beak-like mouths, they fed on the living coral tissues, but such was their destructive power, each year for the past five years the local gang of parrotfish had reduced a ton of coral to fine sand on every acre of reef.

Young bandit angelfish darted amongst the coral heads. White-tip reef sharks rested under coral ledges, and a six-foot long green moray eel eased itself from its bolthole and eyed a slow-moving puffer fish. A huge string of salp, a colonial organism resembling a long transparent tube, drifted in the slow current, while clouds of jack swirled this way and that, one a leader, the rest simply followers. A green sea turtle sank to the sandy sea floor, its legs outstretched and its head and neck raised up. Tiny fish – cleaner wrasse – darted out and busied about its body, stripping it clean of parasites and flaking skin. An orange sea fan provided an anchor for cleaner shrimps waiting for their next client to swim in.

The two whales swam on. A remora adopted Knucklehead for a while, following his every move. When a reef shark chanced by, it changed its allegiance. The young whale may offer a safe umbrella under which to hide, but it would not have provided a meal; better the scraps from a shark's table than none at all. A large barracuda emerged from an old and decaying wreck, hovered in the water and watched the whales swim by. Content that they were neither food nor foe, it turned and continued its unvarying patrol.

The two whales then came upon a humpback whale's fluke,

resting almost flat on the surface of the sea, its owner's vast body seeming to hang from the tail in the water below, its head pointing at the sea floor. It was a female. Her large rounded shape indicated she was pregnant and her lethargy suggested she was near term. A male escort swam nearby. He was not the unborn baby's father but an opportunistic male. He emitted a series of bubbling rumbles and they raised flukes and dived below. She was not yet ready to give birth. She would wait until sundown.

Knucklehead and his mother had travelled for several miles. They were well clear of any oil danger and entering a section of coast they had not visited before. Another solitary bull approached and joined the pair. No other males were in the immediate vicinity, so the large and powerful escort just tagged along peacefully, shadowing the two whales for the rest of the day. Come late afternoon, things began to liven up again.

Heading straight towards them was a female whale with two boisterous male escorts, the larger of the two swimming directly beside her. The trio picked up speed, the secondary escort persistently colliding with his larger neighbour. The commotion attracted two more whales, both smaller males and probably immature, but it did not prevent them from harassing the primary escort. More whales appeared, increasing the group to eight. They were all swimming at speed beside the female.

One of the bulls swam on top of the largest male and pushed down his head. He responded with a burst of bubbles, and the smaller whale dropped back. Another came from below, raking the razor-sharp barnacles on his rostrum against the large whale's softer underside. By this time, the group were travelling at close to 15 miles per hour, a fair speed through such a dense medium as water. Suddenly the female changed direction and her belligerent entourage struggled to maintain their positions alongside. They were now heading straight for Knucklehead.

With three or four pumps of his tail flukes, he swam rapidly to the other side of his mother just as the group ploughed by, the other whales clearly oblivious to him or his mother. Their own escort turned and left them, joining the chase. He barged his way between the smaller males, while two of them peeled off and thwacked each other with flukes and flippers, a sideshow to the main event. Suddenly, they stopped their brawling and quietly swam away. The rest of the group continued their fighting, the female criss-crossed the reef, the others following her every move. Eventually, the smaller whales dropped back and gradually peeled away until the female and the largest and most powerful male remained. His back was rubbed raw from being hammered by the encrustations on the chins of the other bulls. The female slowed to a halt. Little did Knucklehead and his mother know of the tragedy that was about to ensue.

The female mixed up in the chase was pregnant and had not yet given birth. She was a late arrival and her baby was far from ready to be born, but the stress of the courtship battle caused her to abort. The baby was smaller than a full-term humpback baby, usually about the same length as the mother's head, but it was alive…just. Its mother, probably thinking her baby was dead, abandoned it. It swam with difficulty towards the shore and quickly found itself in the surf no more than 50 yards from the beach. Local surfers spotted it and raised the alarm. Swimmers along Puamana Beach were ordered from the water, and with good reason. It was then that the sharks arrived. The tiger sharks had returned.

They had been swimming from island to island, searching for food, when they detected birthing fluids in the sea. Ever alert to a feeding opportunity, they worked their way up-current, testing the water first with one nostril and then the other, zigzagging across the slick of enticing smells until they came to the place where the baby whale had been born prematurely. It was then

29

that they picked up the vibrations of the struggling whale, and they moved closer to the shore.

The sharks were big, one all of 16 feet long – a sea monster. It pushed its broad, blunt snout against the baby, checking for palatability, before withdrawing cautiously and swimming back and forth outside the surf line. A smaller shark rushed in to take an exploratory bite, and the whale thrashed about, causing it to retreat. By now, the whale had been pushed into shallower water, its frail body bruised and battered by the surf. Its skin was scraped on the underlying reef and blood began to seep into the sea. The sharks raised their game a notch. They would dart in, take a bite and withdraw, using the swirl of the surf to carry them onto the whale and the pull of the undertow to take them out and into deeper water.

People had begun to gather on the beach. They looked on in horror at the scene unfolding in front of them. Some dashed into the surf, but the prospect of a head-to-head with a large tiger shark sent even the most foolhardy back to the beach.

'Call the police,' cried one man, realising the moment he spoke that no human intervention was likely to help this baby whale.

'Throw stones', suggested another, and they all threw rocks and pebbles to try to scare away the sharks, but they simply continued their unwavering patrol, waiting for their victim to float out again. The spectators felt helpless. There was little they could do.

With great effort, the young whale remained afloat. It swam up and down slowly along the water's edge, the sharks following its every move, but with a sudden loud and explosive breath – almost a sigh – from its blowhole, it seemed to give up the fight. It floated back in, pushed onto the beach by the waves. People rushed to help, trying to guide the baby back out to sea, but when the police arrived the whale was dead, and more people came to stare.

By evening, the weather had turned. Sun gave way to showers, but the wind was light and a gentle ocean swell crashed on the shore. The sky was filled with white-tailed tropicbirds, the same birds that had set out that morning. They were returning from a successful day's fishing on the ocean, but their arrival had not gone unnoticed. The pirates were waiting, not the swashbuckling kind, but birds – magnificent frigate birds. They had flown in from Tern Island, about 700 miles away in the northwest of the Hawaiian Archipelago. More usually they pluck squid and flying fish from the ocean surface, but when they put their mind to it they can be downright ruthless.

The black males with their red throat-pouches and the females with white underbellies swooped down out of the sun. With a wingspan of six feet or more and deeply forked tails, they were formidable assailants and remarkably skilled flyers. The tropicbirds had little chance. The invaders used speed and extraordinary manoeuvrability to out-fly their victims. Twisting and turning sharply in mid-air, they pecked viciously at the back of the tropicbirds' necks or grabbed wing tips and tail feathers in order to knock them off balance. They pressed home their attacks until their victims regurgitated the day's catch. Effortlessly, the frigate birds scooped up the falling morsels and swallowed them themselves. Time and time again, they flew at the tropicbirds, but now so many were swarming in from the sea some made it through the gauntlet and safely home to their cliffside roosts.

A sleeping giant, the dormant volcano Haleakala, had made the cliffs here. It last erupted in 1790, the same year that King Kamehameha invaded Maui and united the islands under one king. The crater is so huge the entire island of Manhattan would have fitted in the top. Apollo astronauts used this lunar landscape to practise their moon landings.

It was also here, 10,000 feet above the sea, that the demigod Maui snared the sun and forced it to slow its journey across the sky, but this day an even more miraculous event occurred. In the cool evening air, the summit area pushed up through the clouds like another island in a feathery sea, and on its barren cinder slopes a silversword was flowering early in the season. It seemed the low rosette of succulent, sword-shaped leaves had been dipped in liquid silver. They had been growing for over 50 years, then, at an unknown signal, the plant had sent up a stalk of 600 maroon ray flowers and as many again disc flowers. It was over 12 feet high, an unexpected beacon in a lunar landscape. Tiny black-and-yellow bees, more like wasps than bees, swarmed around the florets, making the best of the evening light. They were the plant's pollinators, for other crawling insects were barred from reaching the flowers by minute, sticky hairs. Their toil would be short lived. Having reached its zenith, the entire silversword was about to die and return its nutrients and its seeds to the earth – many decades of preparation for a few moments of glory.

The plant only grows in Hawaii and nowhere else in the world, and by rights it should not have been there at all. It was back from the dead. By 1922, the endemic silverswords on Maui were brought to the brink of extinction. Grazing by cattle and goats destroyed the plant's shallow roots, and the local tradition of taking a flower to prove a person had reached the summit had almost been its downfall. Simply touching its leaves destroys the tiny hairs that protect the plant from the sun and dehydration. Such a simple, seemingly innocuous act condemned the silversword to a slow death.

* * *

As darkness enveloped the islands, the clouds parted and myriad stars scarred the May night sky. It was to be a night of stirring, a night when the world was on the move. Tiny silhouettes of early migrants crossed the face of the full moon. They were golden plovers that had spent the winter in the Hawaiian Archipelago and were heading out on the mid-Pacific flyway, powering along at 30 miles per hour or more to reach their breeding grounds to the northwest of Lake Iliamna in southwestern Alaska. They were not alone. Bristlethighed curlews, leaving from the northwestern part of the island chain, joined the transoceanic procession. Their long journey would take them to the Nulato Hills near the Yukon-Kuskokwim river delta.

The moon had stirred other movements too, tiny almost imperceptible movements. The coral polyps were swelling slightly. Then, one by one, they released their pearl-like eggs and clouds of sperm, an entire reef spawning at the same time on that same night. Soon, the sea was filled with the prospect of new life, creating a surreal upside-down snowstorm as millions upon millions of eggs floated towards the surface. Then, the sponges started too, thickening the white soup. Visibility changed from 100 feet to a thick fog. It was one of the biggest moonlit sex events in the archipelago!

Knucklehead stirred as first one and then another shape slowly passed him in the sea. They were moving in a different direction to the birds, but their business was just as urgent. They were hawksbill sea turtles, one of the two turtles species that live in and around the Hawaiian Archipelago. They feed on sponges. At no more than three feet long and weighing just over 100 pounds, the hawksbill is one of the smaller sea turtles, and these were females on their way from the coral reefs to deposit their eggs on a nearby beach. They were early arrivals. The main emergence was not for another month. On the reefs, they are relatively safe from their number one enemy, the tiger shark, but now they were heading into hazardous waters.

The first of the turtles reached the shore safely, and as she left the water the entire weight of her own body pushed down on her lungs. She wheezed and coughed as she dragged her bulk across the wet sand, huge glutinous tears hanging down from the corners of her eyes. The beach she came to was the same beach on which she had hatched many years before. It shelved steeply so she had not had to travel far from the water's edge to her chosen nest site. Inch by painstaking inch, she headed for the drier areas at the top of the beach, searching for a spot where vegetation fringing the sand would offer some protection. She pushed her nose into the sand, as if testing its suitability, its dampness or dryness. Then, she began to dig. Using her rear flippers, she dug a hole and then began to drop in her eggs, first one at a time, then a dozen in a rush. When 100 or so eggs had been laid, she used her back flippers to cover them with sand, and then dragged herself painfully slowly back to the sea.

This was her first visit this year, but it would not be her last. At 10-day intervals, she would haul herself across the beach seven more times before her job was done. And if that were not enough, when she left the beach for the last time, male turtles would be waiting for her offshore, ready to mate. Finally, she would head for deeper water and rest on the sea floor, completely exhausted by her two-month ordeal.

Other turtles were already not fairing well. During a court-ship scuffle, a clutch of male turtles harassing a female failed to spot the shark. They were swimming at her aggressively, butting and biting her until one clambered onto her back. The shark had been attracted to the commotion in the water, and commotion meant food. It circled slowly at a distance, waiting for the right moment to attack. Gradually, it gained confidence and tightened its circle, but the turtles were so distracted, they were unaware of the danger.

The shark made its move. It was all of 15 feet long, yet it swam with sudden extraordinary speed. It grabbed a turtle's flipper in its toothy maw and shook its head violently from side to side, slicing through flesh and bone. The entire limb was removed, right up to the body. The rest of the turtles fled, but this turtle could not escape, and the shark's first mugging gave it the reassurance it needed to press home its attack. This was an edible target and it was not fighting back. It attacked again and again, taking off the turtle's head in one enormous bite. Blood and body fluids spilled into the water and spread down-current. More sharks were attracted to the feast, reef sharks and more tigers. They flashed past the other turtles, ignoring them. They were only interested in the source of all that blood.

Knucklehead and his mother found themselves in the slick. At this distance from the dead turtle it could be barely detected, but the sharks have an exceptionally sensitive sense of smell. They can detect the equivalent of a drop of blood in an Olympic-sized swimming pool, and two huge tiger sharks had done just that. Believing the source of blood was the two whales, they began to circle them, ready to test their tastiness. The larger of the two whales manoeuvred suddenly. She had picked up the danger, and she was alert. Knucklehead had barely time to slip off his mother's snout when she slewed her huge body towards the aggressors. They swam rapidly away and into the darkness. The rest of the night passed quietly, at least for Knucklehead and his mother.

And this was how it was for the remainder of their time in Hawaii – lazy days and busy nights. Knucklehead was putting on weight fast. As regular as clockwork, he nuzzled close to the teats on the underside of his mother's body and received as much as 120 gallons of thick, creamy milk each day, an enormous quantity in human terms. The young whale drank more in one day than a human does in a year. He was growing fast. More importantly he was increasing his girth. He had to ensure he put on fat – thick blubber, and plenty of it. Where he and his mother were going would be a far cry from balmy Hawaii.

35

CHAPTER THREE
TRAPPED!

During the night, strong winds had blown Portuguese men-of-war, goose barnacles and other floating debris onto the beach. All around, tiny tracks led to small holes in the sand. Two front legs appeared from one hole, followed by the tip of an eyestalk. Satisfied that the coast was clear, their owner emerged. It was a ghost crab, and it clutched an armful of sand. It discarded its load and dived quickly back into its tunnel ready to carry out another.

This was a ghost crab neighbourhood, and its inhabitants were almost invisible, their pale sand-coloured bodies blending in with the sandy background. They were scuttling about, rushing to the sea to wet their gills and gathering food on the tide line. All their frantic activity was confined to the hours before dawn and after dusk, so as the fragments of shells and coral that made up the white sand beach turned gradually from yellow-grey to glaring white gold from the rising sun, the crabs disappeared into their burrows. Their large eyes on short stalks may have enabled them to see 360° around them, but they could not see up, and that was where their main predators were, the ubiquitous gulls.

Out at sea, the distinctive blows of whales had disappeared too. There was no breaching, no tail slaps, and no spyhopping.

Most of the whales had gone. Knucklehead and his mother were among the last to go. They had joined the tail end of a long procession of humpback whales, all heading north. They were going to Alaska for the summer.

The two whales set off before dawn, negotiating the Pailolo Channel between the islands of Maui and Molokai, the windiest and roughest channel in the archipelago. West Maui was enveloped in cloud, and the trade winds were blowing strong – 35 knots and seas of 18 feet. As they passed Moku Hooniki Island, the whales and their blows could barely be seen. For Knucklehead, the breaking waves were a new experience. Each time he surfaced to take a breath the spray would blow over him. It was difficult to breathe, but he was getting the hang of it. A pod of spinner dolphins crowded around. They were the same group that romped with the newly born whale, but this time play was far from on their mind. They were returning from a night's fishing, and making for sheltered bays to rest during the day. In a chorus of squeals and whistles, they were gone, a noisy farewell.

By sunrise, the whales were dwarfed by the sea cliffs on Molokai's north coast, the highest sea cliffs in the world. They tower 3,000 feet over the Pacific Ocean and are etched by silvery waterfalls dropping 500 feet or more to the beach below. Cape Halawa was well behind them. It was the last land they would see for several weeks. They were in the open ocean. No more research boats. No other whales. They were on their own. Their destination was southeast Alaska, but how they find their way was and still is something of a mystery.

Most likely Knucklehead's mother was guided by the Earth's magnetic field, but whatever method of navigation she was using it was remarkably accurate. During the first third of their journey they headed north, wavering little more than a degree either side of magnetic north. They had not been long in the open ocean, however, when a small turtle swam passed. It was not travelling towards Hawaii or away from it. It had come from the west and was heading to the east. Then, another appeared...and another. They were all following the same course. They were loggerheads...youngsters, and they were on a truly astounding migration. They were travelling from Yakushima in southern Japan, where they hatched, to feeding grounds off the coast of Baja, Mexico, where they would be joining many others of their own kind to feed on pelagic red crabs.

They had set out as turtles no bigger than your hand, and by the time they reached Hawaii they were halfway through their staggering six-year journey. If they were travelling direct, this excursion across the Pacific would be over 7,000 miles, but these little turtles were not following a straight line. For many weeks, they rode around eddies, resembling gigantic under-water cyclones, getting off these natural carousels at exactly the same point they got on. When back on course they pushed forward at a speed of a fraction of a mile-an-hour, to move slowly but steadily towards their destination; and they were not alone out here.

Scattered over the sea surface was a raft of sooty shearwaters. They had stopped off on their annual migration from nesting sites on sub-Antarctic islands near New Zealand to feeding sites bordering the Arctic, another extraordinary journey of nearly 40,000 miles – the longest journey made by any bird migrant. The shearwaters dived down amongst the two whales, picking off small fish and squid. Most were diving to 40 feet, but some birds went down to 200 feet or more.

The waters here were surprisingly productive. The open ocean is more usually considered a barren 'desert', but here were fish, squid, seabirds and turtles thriving in a corridor of unexpected plenty stretching across the middle of the Pacific

Ocean. They were all there because this is where major ocean currents meet. They coincide roughly with the subtropical frontal zone to the north of the Hawaii Archipelago, between 25° and 30° North. In effect, Knucklehead and his mother were crossing a great transoceanic highway and it was busy.

A half-a-mile further on and a sailfish – the fastest fish in the sea – flashed passed the two whales. Its fins were held flush with the body for speed and energy efficiency, but then it slowed abruptly, held its pectoral fins out and raised its enormous dorsal fin. It had picked up the unmistakeable vibrations of panicking fish. It eased forward slowly, its fins still erect, alert for danger.

A group of Pacific spotted dolphins were milling about below an enormous shoal of tens of thousands of mackerel. The mackerel were here to feed on the clouds of mysid shrimps and fish larvae that had been feeding on the bloom of phytoplankton along the boundary of a large eddy. The fish were now prey themselves for much larger creatures, but to make it worth their while the dolphins had to concentrate the fish. They swam back and forth below the shoal, herding it slowly towards the surface. Its shape changed constantly, first a huge, constantly moving sphere, then a revolving cylinder that folded in on itself to become a dense ball of writhing fish once more. It was instant death to be outside the shoal, so each fish tried to move to the centre.

The sailfish took one look, folded its fins and accelerated at an amazing speed into the fish ball. At the same time its body changed from uniformly silver to vivid dark blue stripes. It slashed with its long, sword-like bill, turned rapidly and made another run. Injured fish were left behind as the fish ball moved through the ocean. The sailfish scooped them up and was gone.

The dolphins meanwhile picked fish from the great streaming and squirming carousel. Mackerel on the outside edge seemed weakened and disorientated, unable to keep up with the rest of the shoal. They had been sprayed continuously with powerful bursts of high-pitched sounds from the dolphin's echolocation system and, perhaps, this had delivered knockout blows that debilitated the fish, making them easier to catch.

By this time, the disturbance had reached the surface. The mackerel boiled over, and shearwaters were not slow to recognise a feeding frenzy. They swarmed in from the surrounding ocean, and plunged into the water. From below, it resembled a surreal underwater ballet, and all in slow motion. The birds, silhouetted against the surface, appeared to fly and glide through the water. Each bird grabbed a struggling fish and manipulated it in its bill before drifting back up to the surface.

Seemingly out of nowhere, a school of yellowfin tuna burst onto the scene. They tore into the mackerel, grabbing anything in their path. They came from all directions and at high speed, but they did not collide. Before too long, what was once a gigantic shoal of mackerel was reduced to a handful of isolated groups. The dolphins drifted away and the tuna raced off to feed elsewhere. The survivors sank slowly to deeper water, yet the shearwaters still pressed home their attacks, going to the very limit of their underwater capability. At that point even they were forced to leave their quarry.

It was then that an enormous sei whale appeared. It was over 50 feet long. It swam up rapidly from the depths with its enormous mouth agape and its throat's pleats spread, taking most of what remained in one enormous gulp before swimming away into the distance. A few twitching bodies, a slick of fish oil and a shower of shimmering scales was all that was left.

The odour drifted down current and was picked up by a blue shark. With its sleek, streamlined body and long pectoral fins it was arguably the most beautiful of sharks. It had been diving deep in pursuit of squid, and had returned to the surface waters to warm up. Following the direction of the drifting oil droplets it came to the site of the massacre, scooping up the larger scraps. Eventually, there was no more, and it made a long glide back down to the depths to pursue the school of deep-sea squid.

Knucklehead and his mother had missed the spectacle. They had pushed on, and would have to wait a deal longer for their first meal. An isolated fish ball in the open ocean might whet the appetite of a passing sei whale, but it would not satisfy a hungry humpback. His mother needed fish in the quantities that were found off Alaska. There was renewed urgency in their progress. Despite Knucklehead's relatively small size and inexperience in travelling long distances, they were covering nearly 100 miles a day.

* * *

It was late afternoon when they encountered a pod of sperm whales. Knucklehead was confronted suddenly with an entire wall of whales, each the size and shape of a bus. This defensive formation, however, was not a response to the two humpbacks; the real concern was a pod of 30 short-finned pilot whales that had slipped in behind them. The smaller whales were in small groups and spread out across the ocean. One sub-group swam parallel to Knucklehead and his mother. It buzzed them and left. The rest focused on the sperm whale group. Several of the sperm whales had white tooth marks on their tail flukes and strands of skin were hanging from the trailing edges. They had been in a fight, and Knucklehead and his mother had swum straight into the centre of it.

The pilot whales surfaced frequently and left the water in shallow leaps, and some particularly large members of the pod approached the head of one of the sperm whales and thrashed at it with their tail flukes. The sperm whales reacted by taking

41

up a second defence formation close to the surface, this time with their heads at the centre and tails facing outwards like the spokes of wheel – the so-called 'marguerite' formation because it resembled the flower. Some whales positioned themselves vertically so the marguerite had a three-dimensional shape, and it formed and reformed in response to the pilot whale attacks.

The pilot whales were undeterred. They swam over the backs of the sperm whales and along their flanks in order to get to the centre. They were looking for calves. Sperm whales protect their calves by keeping them at the centre of the rosette, but there were no calves here. The sperm whales had open mouths, their teeth and white mouth and lips clearly visible. They blew clouds of bubbles from their blowholes and swept their tail flukes sideways through the water or slapped them flat on the surface. The pilot whales harried them like terriers, probing this way and that, testing them to see their strengths and weaknesses.

A cacophony of whistles and clicks announced the arrival of a group of bottlenose dolphins. They must have picked up the sounds of the skirmish. Wherever there was a fight, you could expect bullyboy bottlenoses and here they were; and they were not alone. The false killers had turned up too. They circled the sperm whales in a clockwise fashion, but for the larger sperm whales all this was getting too much. They defecated into the water and dived into the abyss, out of harm's way. The smaller whales could not follow. The sperm whales could dive down two miles, and could hold their breath for a couple of hours. The pilot whales could go no further than to 2,000 feet and bottlenose dolphins to 1,000 feet, so there was no point in following. They all thrashed about in the cloud for a few minutes and then left. Knucklehead and his mother, meanwhile, had made a fast exit; and not a moment too soon.

A couple of large oceanic white-tip sharks appeared. They

had spade-like fins with distinct white tips. They had been following the pilot whales, even eating their faeces. Meals out here were often few and far between, and the pilot whales with their echolocation system were especially talented at finding shoals of fish and squid. The sharks knew it and followed them. The pilot whale pod was also like a moving 'blind' in which the sharks could hide. It enabled these slow-swimming sharks to hijack large fast-swimming fish, such as swordfish or marlin. They would not see the whales as a threat and might approach more closely. All the sharks needed do was to dash out and grab them.

The oceanic white-tips were especially bold, and were quick to investigate anything that smacked of food. They had an extraordinary sense of smell, and had sniffed not only the sea but also the air for signs of a meal. They pushed their snouts above the surface and took down bubbles of smells in their convoluted nostrils. Airborne smells moved more quickly than those in the water, so the oceanic white-tips had the edge on their competitors. They were always first to a whale carcass, should one be floating at the surface. This time, however, they were last to arrive, and there was very little to keep them there.

Each of the sharks was preceded by a gaggle of black-and-white striped pilot fish. As their larger companions nosed around the sperm whale effluent, testing and tasting, the pilot fish found small particles of food floating in the water, but with nothing substantial, the sharks and their pilot fish moved on too, catching up the pilot whales on their endless wandering across the Pacific.

A large school of silky sharks replaced the white-tips. They too had picked up the telltale signs of a commotion in the water and were here to investigate its cause. Wary of the more powerful oceanic white-tips, the silkies had mooched around the periphery, waiting for their rivals to leave. The smell of the sperm whale faeces had been so strong and they were unable to resist it. They mouthed the cloudy water, swimming rapidly in and out of the dissipating cloud, but there was nothing to be had so they disappeared too.

By this time Knucklehead and his mother were over a mile away, and they were making good speed. Each time the older whale surfaced, her heart-shaped spout shot 10 to 20 feet into the air. It was a mist of warm moist air, oily mucus from her lungs, and the seawater she had cleared from her twin blow-holes. In the course of a few seconds, she exchanged over 2,500 gallons of air, 90 per cent of her lung capacity in two seconds. Each of her lungs was the size of a small car and, such was the rapidity with which the exchange took place, the air entered or left at a speed of 300 miles per hour. Unlike humans, who breathe without thinking, Knucklehead's mother was conscious of when and when not to breathe. The area of skin around her blowhole was sensitive to the presence or absence of water, indicating when the blowhole was clear of the water. On migration the adult whale was taking a breath every five minutes or so, her calf a little more frequently.

* * *

By the end of the first day, the wind had subsided and the ocean was no longer angry and topped with white horses. Smooth water stretched to the horizon in all directions; no land for hundreds of miles. They were in the middle of the Pacific Ocean, just two of several thousand humpback whales on the move. Some were en route from Hawaii to Russia, via the Aleutian Islands. Others were going even further, into the chilly Bering Sea. Most of the whales from Hawaii were heading for Alaska, where migrants from Japan and Baja California would be joining them for the summer.

At sunset, Knucklehead and his mother slowed to rest. The sea had remained calm and, like two enormous logs, they rose and fell with the swell, drifting slowly in the weak ocean current. While travelling north, they had crossed narrow bands of moving water. Those flowing from east to west alternated with those flowing west to east. Now, they were in an eastward flow, drifting at less than a tenth of a mile per hour. It was edging them ever so slowly towards the North American mainland.

The darkness overtook them and the water all around began to fill with life once more. The creatures of the deep were rising to the surface. In some places there were so many animals on the move they appeared as a solid layer – the 'deep scattering layer' – on the sonar screens of passing ships, almost as if the bottom of the sea were rising up to the surface.

At the same time each night, these vertical travellers arrived on cue, a mixed bag of deep-sea creatures – fish, squid, jelly-fish, and shrimps – which rose from the depths and headed for the surface. The daylight hours were spent hiding in the twilight zone, over a thousand feet below the surface. They bided their time there, trying to be inconspicuous, trying to remain alive. The darkness was a refuge, and come the evening they swam up to the plankton-rich surface waters to feed. The distance they travelled each morning and night was the equivalent of a human running a marathon before breakfast and again before supper.

How they knew when to head towards the surface was something of a mystery. It could not have been changes in light intensity or on a cloudy day they would have started off at the wrong time, and different organisms set off at different times anyway. Whatever the trigger, they had arrived, and swarms of tiny lights gathered around the two whales. They were lanternfish, probably the most common group of fishes in the deep sea. They were so numerous that they alone could account for the rising deep scattering layer. Each fish had a bluntly rounded head with huge eyes and rows of light-producing organs along the lower sides of its body. The brightness of the lights matched the intensity of the ambient light, no more than starlight on this moonless night. Viewed from below, from where its predators were likely to approach, it blended in with any light from the surface – a form of bioluminescent camouflage.

On this night the ruse was not working. As if on cue, a school of blue-finned tuna appeared. These huge fish, each over eight feet long and weighing more than 200 pounds, are among the biggest and fastest fish in the Pacific. They have been clocked at over 30 miles per hour in 10- to 20-second dashes, and they were making full use of that speed. They made short work of a patch of diminutive lanternfish, before continuing on their way. They had already crossed the entire width of the Pacific three times in 600 days, and travelled nearly 25,000 miles, and they were not stopping now.

The usual cloud of blood and scales marked the site of the carnage, but the night-time cavalcade had only just begun. Comb jellies drifted in the current. Some were less than an inch long. They were no more than gelatinous sacs with a pair of retractable tentacles that captured copepods and the minuscule larvae of fish and crustaceans. Eight rows of motile hair cells, stretching the length of the body, provided limited propulsion. The tiny hairs were like the oars of an ancient trireme, except that the movement rippled down the body like a 'Mexican wave'. By altering the beat frequency of one or more of the rows, the comb jelly changed direction. A small deep-sea fish nosed a comb jelly and received a face full of red ink for its trouble. It was a tiny shark, no longer than six inches and its tail end glowed in the dark. It was a dwarf lanternshark, probably the smallest shark in the world.

Knucklehead stirred. He felt something large moving in the water nearby. A dark shape was heading his way. It was another shark, but this one was big, over 16 feet long, and it looked like no other shark the baby whale had seen. Most obvious was its mouth. It was huge and surrounded by thick, rubbery lips that glowed in the dark – a light trap. As it passed, Knucklehead moved towards his mother, but he was in no danger. It was megamouth, a filter feeder. It was more interested in shrimps, copepods and jellyfish and not young whales. It descended slowly, and was lost. Its deep-sea shrimp-like prey was more usually found a thousand feet down.

It was time to move on. Knucklehead's mother shivered noticeably as she started up. She pushed with her great tail flukes and she was off. A swarm of neon flying squid overtook her. They were on migration too. Like the whales, they were travelling from subtropical spawning grounds near Hawaii to feeding sites close to the Alaskan coast. As Knucklehead caught up with his mother she changed course towards the northeast, and they swam into the night.

*   *   *

A wind blew up at sunrise, and the ocean surface had a fair chop. They were heading into an area of low pressure at whose centre the winds were being whipped up to 50 knots and the waves were up to 30 feet high. It was beginning to rain. As the two whales ploughed on through the water and surfaced to breathe, they were lifted high on a crest one minute and sank low into a trough the next. Then a wave took them and Knucklehead and his 30-ton mother were surfing. They used the energy provided by the sea and then plunged below.

Knucklehead's mother was not as streamlined as some of the other baleen whales. The fin whale, for instance, is a combined sprinter and long-distance runner. It has a long, sleek body that slides through the water at a top speed of 30 miles per hour when alarmed, and a cruising speed of 16 miles per hour, making it the fastest of the large whales. The large female humpback, by contrast, generally moved at five miles per hour and slowed to as little as one mile per hour on her migration. Seen from above, her snout was broad and rounded, while in profile it was more slender. The top of her snout and lower jaw were lined with bumps, called tubercles. They were actually hair follicles, each with at least one stiff hair that probably detected movement in the water ahead. There were also patches of barnacles.

Under the lower jaw were long lines of ventral or throat grooves, which stretched back to her belly, halfway along her body. These would be more evident on the feeding grounds. They enabled the whale to expand her mouth and throat when feeding. On her back she had a stubby dorsal fin. Its shape varied from whale to whale and sat on a hump, one origin of the whale's common English name. At the rear, her body narrowed to a slender peduncle or tailstock that broadened to tail flukes 18 feet across. They had pointed tips and a distinct indentation in the middle. Her most notable feature, though, was the pair of flippers or pectoral fins, known as 'pecs' to whale scientists. They were a third of the length of her body, and they enabled her to negotiate tight turns. She and her kind were the most manoeuvrable of all the large whales.

* * *

Later that day, mother and son had reached the Tufts Abyssal Plain, a very deep, flat area of the North Pacific, about 400 miles across and due west of Seattle. The seabed was three miles down, and directly below them, close to the bottom, was a

Tufts' speciality, a deep-sea umbrella octopus with a striking resemblance to Walt Disney's *Dumbo*. It had a soft, gelatinous body and fins that looked like the ears of the flying elephant. It hovered over the sea floor while searching for worms, molluscs and crustaceans in the bottom ooze. It moved by flapping its 'ears' and pulsating its webbed arms like a jellyfish. It was one of the rarest octopuses in the world, and it shared its deep-sea home with a ship that just would not sink.

Sitting in 10,866 feet of water on the floor of the plain was the front section of a 639-foot-long cargo ship, the *New Carissa*, but how it got there was somewhat bizarre. The freighter initially went aground near the entrance of Coos Bay, Oregon, but oil was leaking badly from the hull and so US Navy demolition experts attempted to burn the fuel on board using explosives and napalm. A huge fire engulfed the ship and much of fuel, but not all, was burned. This weakened the ship's structure and during the next storm it broke into two pieces. During a lull between storms an attempt was made to pump out the remainder of the oil, but it mostly brought out the seawater that had entered the hull. A special mile-long tow rope was flown over from the Netherlands and a tug, the *Sea Victory*, tried to tow the front section out to sea.

After two days its succeeded in floating the ship at high tide, and it was towing it about 50 miles out to sea when the tow rope broke. The bow section drifted back to shore and onto a sandbar 80 miles north of Coos Bay at Patterson Beach State Park. The rope was hastily recovered and the bow section re-floated and towed over 300 miles into the Pacific. Demolition experts put in 400 pounds of directional explosives but when they were set off the bow section was still afloat. A naval destroyer, the *USS David R. Ray*, arrived and fired 69 rounds from its deck gun, but the ship was still floating. Finally – over a month since the ship first went aground – a Los Angeles-class nuclear attack submarine let loose a Mark 48 torpedo and the bow section of the *New Carissa* finally went to its watery grave.

For now, though, something far more sinister was floating in the sea directly ahead of the two whales. It was a 'ghost net', the remnants of a large commercial drift net that was floating along in the ocean currents. It still continued to fish, even though nobody was there to harvest the catch. It had been drifting for months. It was festooned with seaweeds and other organisms, making it a refuge in the open ocean for many small fishes, but a potential death trap for anything bigger. The skeleton of a turtle was wrapped up in the net. It had been picked clean by fishes.

Knucklehead's mother spotted the obstacle and swerved to avoid it. Seeing her manoeuvre, Knucklehead tried to catch her up but as he brought up his tail it caught under one of the hanging ropes. He struggled to get free, but the more he thrashed about, the more he became entangled. He was caught and he was running out of air. With great effort, he found he had just enough slack to reach the surface. He took a gasp and sank back down again. At first she failed to notice that he was not with her, but when his regular touches for reassurance were absent, she realised he had been left behind. She doubled back and found her baby trapped in the net. She gently nudged him to the surface. He took another breath then sank again, thrashed about some more but he could not get free. His mother circled, but she was powerless to help. She nudged him again. He struggled to the surface and then sank again, the rope cutting into the skin of his tailstock. He lay still, while his mother hung in the water nearby.

Several hours passed, by which time the baby whale was becoming increasingly tired; but he was a fighter. He struggled time and again to the surface, took a hasty breath, and then relaxed momentarily. Every time he struggled the rope seemed to be tighter. It cut into his skin, and the gash was burning. Even whales feel pain. Every time a harpoon enters the body of a minke whale, that whale feels pain, excruciating pain. In most civilised countries laws protect pigs, cattle and chickens from experiencing unnecessary pain, stress or injury at slaughter, but there is no law to protect whales.

Knucklehead struggled on. His mother nudged him and urged him and he thrashed and he fought. She moaned and whined and he responded in kind. Long days followed even longer nights, but still the little whale would not give up. They drifted to the southeast, each day taking them closer to the mainland. Gulls dropped down and sat on the sea's surface. Like morbid sentinels, they waited for the baby whale to rise up to breathe and then scrambled onto his back and picked at his skin. Every time he surfaced, they squabbled, each fighting for the right to pick at the sores. Knucklehead lashed out as best he could, but the birds just kept coming, their cacophony deafening.

After what seemed an eternity, the whales heard a deep throbbing sound and it was getting louder. It was a boat and it was heading their way. An aircraft had spotted the commotion in the water and radioed a coastguard cutter to investigate.

As the boat hove to alongside the floating net, divers went over the side to check on the health of the baby whale. The mother moved beside Knucklehead. The divers came out of the water immediately lest they be crushed. This was not going to be easy, and the sea was roughing up. The mother whale moved away, and the divers went down again. Ropes were not only around his tail but also in his mouth and wrapped around his body. By now the wind had picked up and the waves were making rescue impossible. The divers clambered aboard, but not before they attached a tracking device to the young whale so they could find him again. They were forced to return to base until the storm had passed.

By next morning, the wind had dropped and Knucklehead lopped gently in the ocean swell. Not long after first light the coastguards reappeared and divers went down again. The young whale struggled, but its will to live was gradually waning. The humans would have to be quick. Again, they went into the water, avoiding the mother's tail and the thrashing calf, and began to cut the net and ropes. They were making some headway when a dark torpedo shape appeared. It buzzed one of the divers and his buddy fended off the attack with a stick. It was a shark, the fastest in the sea and the most intelligent. It was a shark with attitude – a mako. It swam about rapidly, searching for the source of blood. It was Knucklehead's tail. The divers came out of the water once more. It was not safe to be down with an excitable mako.

The mother, sensing the danger, turned rapidly and smashed her tail down on the sea's surface, again and again. The shark swam rapidly around, dodging the blows but eventually it gave up and went in search of easier prey. The divers went back into the water and continued to hack at the net. Progress was slow. Their knives blunted within minutes on the tough polyfilament line. They formed a chain gang – some divers sharpening knives on the boat, and they passed them to others cutting in the water.

The whale had certainly got himself in a tangle. His mother circled around, but did not interfere. The divers hacked. Knucklehead struggled, and then they hacked some more. And then, suddenly he was free. With a thrust of his tail he was beside his mother. The lead diver surfaced and called to his colleagues on the boat.

'We have saved a whale!'

A cheer went up and, before they had time to turn and look, the whales had gone.

CHAPTER FOUR
ISLANDS AT THE EDGE
OF THE WORLD

A dense fog blanketed sea and shore. The morning was still and eerily quiet: no surf, few birds and just the muffled lapping of water on rocks. A fish jumped, pursued by some unseen danger, leaving telltale rings that spread across the mirror-calm surface. A plover, grounded by the fog, probed the tide line for titbits, a wily gull watching its every move, ready to snatch a morsel if it had half a chance. A foghorn broke through briefly from a distant ship, only to be replaced by the heavy silence.

By the time Knucklehead and his mother were in sight of the coast, though, the sun began to burn through and the mist was lifting, but there were no signs of other whales. While the youngster was caught in the net, they had drifted closer to the North American mainland but somewhat to the south of his mother's traditional migration route. They were approaching Canada's Queen Charlotte Islands, known locally as *Haida Gwaii* meaning 'islands of the people', a 200 million-year-old buckle in the Earth's crust that was pushed up as the Pacific tectonic plate disappeared below North America. They rounded the untidy string of islands at Cape St James to find themselves fighting a five knot current. For a moment they seemed to be going backwards rather than forwards, but a determined surge saw them heading slowly northwards again.

They were greeted by a deafening discord of honking and barking. Underwater, dark torpedo shapes raced around them as they swam. They were Steller's sea lions, the biggest of all the sea lions and this colony was one of the largest on North America's west coast. Hundreds were draped over rocky ledges or packed onto crowded beaches, and downwind the smell was overpowering. It was approaching the breeding season, and the large bulls, each weighing almost a ton and recognisable immediately by their imposing lion-like manes, were rounding up the hapless females into harems. The escapees at sea mobbed Knucklehead and his mother. Such was their curiosity, they swam to within an inch of the whales' heads before turning in a great arc and then swooping in, around and out, again and again. Then, all of a sudden they were gone, their places taken by even larger shapes. The black-and-white patterns were unmistakeable...orcas...killer whales.

The pod was almost silent; no screams or whistles, just the occasional stream of clicks. The killers swam close to Knucklehead and he moved instinctively towards his mother. She watched them apprehensively. One wrong move and they might attack. One by one they swam parallel to the small whale, took a hard look and moved on. They were killers all right, but not interested in whales...at least not for the moment. They had sea lions in their sights. As one, they submerged, travelled underwater for a short distance and then broke through the surface right beside the sea lion rookery.

A large male orca, his sword-like dorsal fin pointing at the sky, grabbed a young sea lion from right off the rocks and was gone in a second. Patches of blood and fragments of blubber and skin floated to the surface. He reappeared, his victim held firmly in his jaws, then let go, turned rapidly and batted the limp body into the air with his tail. He seemed to be playing with the sea lion, like a cat with a mouse. The rest of the pod formed up in a line, watching intently the inert body floating at the surface. It twitched, a flipper flailing weakly in the air. A female orca broke ranks and raised her body up vertically out of the water – spyhopping – once, then twice as if craning her neck to see what was happening. Two more sea lions appeared and they porpoised towards their stricken comrade. They skirted around and under it, urging it to move. Slowly, it came to life, and the escorts swam in a figure-of-eight pattern, almost supporting its weight as the three of them inched painfully slowly towards the rocky shore. The orcas stood off, witnesses to the wildlife drama unfolding in front of them. None of the pod moved. They remained in their regimented line. The three sea lions finally reached a pile of sea-weathered logs that were heaped untidily on the shore, but just as the stricken one was leaving the water, the male orca burst out of the sea, grabbed it and disappeared below.

The other orcas submerged simultaneously. They had their own game to play. They had spotted something else to harass, not the two humpbacks, but a group of minke whales, the smallest of the baleen whales. They gave chase and the minkes took off at high speed, the killer whales in pursuit. Killer whales might have been the fastest small whales over a short distance but the minkes had stamina. They just kept on going and would have outrun the killers, except that one whale took an unfortunate turn into a confined bay and the pack was on it in seconds. It offered no resistance, and the killers first rammed and then tore into its body.

The large bull orca was not with them. It had doubled back and was moving silently towards the coast. A group of harbour seals was swimming a couple of hundred yards from the shore, and the orca skilfully cut them off from their only means of escape. It stayed underwater, swimming right up to the group, and then burst onto the surface, grabbing a seal by the head. One bite and it was decapitated, but the orca did not stop at that. It raced after another and another, each time either biting the head or squeezing the seal until its guts spewed out. Curiously, it did not feed. It simply left the dead bodies floating on the surface. It was killing just for the sake of killing. Like a fox in a chicken coup, it was surplus killing. The bodies drifted in on the tide. A noisy flock of gulls crowded around, fighting for the tastiest bits.

The two humpbacks moved on, making no more than two miles per hour against the current. They were out of range of the killer whale pod and the aberrant bull. They had reached the southern end of *Gwaii Haanas*, meaning 'place of wonder', a place reputed to be one of the windiest in Canada. Normally it is open to the full fury of the Pacific – 100-knot winds and 30-foot-high seas – but this day it was remarkably still. On the cliffs, horned puffins waited for the right moment to launch into the air. On their faces, the black 'horn' above the eyes was clearly visible and the yellow bill plate was beginning to grow, a sign that the breeding season was about to start. Some birds had already made contact with their partner for life, and were returning from sea to their regular nesting burrows. Fish draped in their bills indicated successful fishing excursions; but they were especially alert when they approached the coast. Bald eagles and peregrines were a constant threat so the puffins took their own kind of evasive action. As they returned from the ocean they joined those that had just taken off, and all the birds circled in a great, noisy gyre over the shallow waters before judging it safe to fly in to the cliffs or out to sea. The returning birds waited for the right moment to make for the cliff tops. Flying over water, they were safe. If a puffin was hit by a bird of prey over water, it would lose its meal to the fishes; but over dry land, the puffins were at their most vulnerable.

Right on cue and almost invisible as it came out of the glare of the sun, a peregrine stooped. It folded its wings and dropped headfirst like a stone. Reaching a staggering 100 miles an hour, it was more like a bullet than a bird. At the last moment it opened its wings, levelled out and hit a puffin on the back of the neck with a spine-breaking jolt. The puffin fell to the rocks below. The peregrine grabbed it in its talons and carried it to a ledge. A flurry of feathers meant the predator was already tearing into the lifeless body of its prey.

The whales were in the lee of Moresby Island, out of the long ocean swell and into Hecate Strait. Here the small, rugged islets are topped with scrappy stands of weather-beaten trees, while along the shore of the main island, coastal temperate rainforest of old-growth cedars and giant spruce trees come right down to the water's edge. Further inland, the forest floor is covered with carpets of green moss. Lush green lichens are draped over branches, and ferns grow in notches in tree trunks. It is the hiding place and nesting site of a small species of seabird – the marbled murrelet.

Most seabirds nested on open spaces, rocks, cliffside ledges, or in burrows, but the marbled murrelet had built its nest on a branch in an ancient tree. Its single egg was balanced on a platform of mosses and lichens over 100 feet from the ground. The female sat, while her mate headed out to sea to feed. He zigzagged low over the water in a manner more like a bee. He was late in leaving. Most of the birds had already set out under cover of darkness. The only sound that betrayed their exodus was a noise reminiscent of a jet plane. It was made by air rushing though their feathers. Some had travelled from sites many miles from the mainland coast, but since the forests on these islands had gained some form of protection and most commercial logging was stopped, some birds had a refuge here on the islands, and there was plenty of food – sand eels, herring and shiner perch – right on their doorstep.

Passing Burnaby Island, Knucklehead's mother raised her flukes and dived to the bottom. The young whale followed. All around, the seabed was littered with bat stars, hundreds, even thousands of them, in a multitude of different hues – turquoise, burgundy, red, purple. Huge strands of brown kelp reached from the sea floor to the surface, alive with red turban shells. Brown sea cucumbers and red multi-armed sunstars lazed amongst the giant holdfasts, and hermit crabs picked daintily at scraps of food washed in by the rushing tide. Dotted here and there were brightly coloured sea anemones, like jewels on the bottom of the sea. Their tentacles waved expectantly in the current for food to drift in.

Without warning, Knucklehead's mother raced for the surface. Bursting through, her body hung momentarily in the air before she crashed back down on her side. She had heard the unmistakeable moans of a humpback whale in the distance. Was it the rest of her herd? Had they reached the feeding grounds?

All around them now were the blows of whales. They were humpbacks all right, and they were feeding, using their long, white pectoral fins to corral fish in the shallows, but the sounds they made were unfamiliar. This was Juan Perez Sound, not the traditional summer feeding grounds of Knucklehead's mother. Reluctantly they continued north.

In the cool, still air, clouds of steam drifted across the water as they passed the aptly named Hot Spring Island – *Gandl K'in*. The water was low, almost 25 feet below the high tide mark, and the rocks laid bare were packed with countless starfishes. Black oystercatchers hammered at mussels, using their thick, red bills, while glaucous-winged gulls busied overhead, waiting for a chance as usual to steal their meal, their *kak-kak-kak* calls and high-pitched wailing warning off rivals. When the whales reached Tanu Island, the starfish were replaced by sea urchins, a carpet of the spiny creatures on the shallow sea floor.

By evening, the sky was clear and the mountains of Louise Island were silhouetted against the setting sun. The days were lengthening, the nights shrinking, but the two whales had travelled not more than 100 miles that day. They still had far to go.

On a remote headland overlooking a wide, crescent-shaped bay, a lone figure sat next to a small dwelling, gazing out to the sea. He was the watchman, one of a family of the Haida people who survived the time of dying in the late 19th century when Europeans brought smallpox to the islands and a civilisation was all but wiped out. Beside him stood several tall totem and mortuary poles carved from trunks of red cedar. They had been there for 100 years, but many were resting now at drunken angles or lying flat against the ground. Mosses and lichens covered some; others were bare and weathered grey. Each was a column of faces and figures piled one on top of the other that told stories of people and animals. There were gigantic thunderbirds that swooped out of the sky to take up giant whales for supper, and whale people who lived in great underwater cities. There were wolves that, when tired of hunting in packs on land, changed into killer whales that hunted in packs under the sea. They conjured up events that took place in a mythical world in which people were transformed into animals and animals into people, at a time not so long ago.

As the last strands of light disappeared from the northern horizon, Knucklehead's mother turned away from the shore and out towards the sea, but a forest of giant kelp and rafts of drifting logs blocked their way. They worked their way around the obstacles, and then they turned north once more, into the darkness. The route was taking them away from the coast. The night passed peacefully; that is, most of the night.

In the early hours, when it was still dark, a deep throbbing echoed through the sea. They could feel it more than hear it. Knucklehead and his mother rose to the surface to breathe and caught a glimpse of bright lights...and they were moving. They dived below and continued to swim. Whales often saw lights like those at sea, but their significance was more than often lost on them. For the mariner at sea, moving lights mean ships and this ship was the Prince Rupert to Skidegate ferry. Three times a week it plied these waters and this night it was on schedule, due to arrive in the islands at six o'clock in the morning. Early tourists were on board, fast asleep in their bunks during the eight-hour journey. The officer of the watch was as unaware of the whales ahead as the whales were of his approaching ship.

The two whales rose and exhaled, the fine mist of their blows shooting into the cool night air. By chance, the officer on board spotted the disturbance and ordered the ship to swing a few degrees to port. The throbbing became louder. The bows swung round. The whales dived. The noise was almost unbearable. On came the ship, nearly 6,000 tons of her. At a speed of 18 knots, she would not change direction quickly. Knucklehead's tail slipped under the surface. He dived for all he was worth. The great dark shape glided over them. The orderly swishing sounds of the propellers replaced the deep hum of the engines, and then the ship was gone. Knucklehead swam for the surface took a breath and followed his mother.

* * *

By late afternoon on the following day, the whales were approaching Rose Spit (*Naii Kun* in the Haida language) at the extreme northeast of Graham Island. The incessant honking of sandhill cranes overhead announced their arrival for the summer. They had travelled the Pacific Flyway, from winter quarters alongside the Sacramento and San Joaquin rivers in California's Central Valley, and were making their way to the head of Masset Inlet to nest and breed in the high intertidal areas at Delkatla Slough. They had raced along, covering up to 500 miles a day, but now they were dropping from their cruising height a mile above the ground, searching out the same patch of ground they occupied the year before. They trumpeted to each other continuously as they flew, each eager to land and find their partner for life. Soon, they would be dancing, prancing, leaping, bowing and throwing sticks and grass in one of the most graceful courtship displays of any northern bird.

Along the shore a small herd of wild cattle nosed about in the grasses beyond the sand dunes. They were domestic stock that had been introduced by settlers but abandoned. Not far away a blacktail deer peered out of a stand of trees, and a hairy woodpecker, recognisable by its black-and-white plumage with a flash of red on the back of its head and its loud 'peek' call, hammered at a piece of loosened bark to get at the grubs hidden underneath. A squirrel scampered across a neighbouring tree, while in a pool on the ground a raccoon washed the sand from its evening meal. Remote from civilisation, the spit and its wildlife were undisturbed.

On the beach, the tide was so low there were long fingers of drying sand separated by parallel rows of long, shallow pools. They were formed in the strong currents when the beach was covered by water. Harbour seals were hauled out and littered the beach, each lying in its curious bowed way, both its head and tail flukes held clear of the ground. A back bear ambled across the spit. They watched its every move, ready to flop back into the sea if it should come too close. It disappeared into the scrub and was not seen again that night.

The whales were making fair speed but not enough. Every hour they were travelling meant an hour less on the feeding grounds, and Knucklehead's mother needed to feed and soon. It was many months ago that she had her last meal. She was quite capable of swimming faster but her young calf slowed her down. As the spit disappeared behind them, they were once more in the open sea and crossing Dixon Entrance, but they were not alone. Other whales, not humpbacks but grey whales, had joined them. They were heading north too, but travelling much further into the Bering Sea and their traditional feeding grounds. They had set out from Baja. Their annual round trip of almost 14,000 miles was the second longest known migration of any mammal.

This party were mothers with calves and they were in a hurry. Their blotched bodies were more streamlined than those of the two humpbacks and they slipped easily through the water. When they surfaced, they blew three or four times at 20-second intervals and then raised their flukes and submerged for up to five minutes. They were making about eight or nine miles per hour and overtook the two humpbacks. They followed a course outside the islands of southeast Alaska and up the Pacific coast. Knucklehead and his mother struck out for the Inside Passage.

* * *

The two whales broke the surface, breathed, and submerged in harmony. It was an unbroken natural rhythm, to which they adhered for hour after exhausting hour on this seemingly endless journey; and there were more travellers all following the same relentless course.

Knucklehead's heart almost missed a beat. One group was black-and-white and look remarkably like killer whales, but they were Dall's porpoises, a pod of 20. At six feet long they were much smaller than killer whales and they lacked the prominent sword-like dorsal fin, having a lower triangular one instead. They were heading for colder water to the north, but with night approaching it was time for them to search for food. Some took a free ride, carried on the pressure wave ahead of the two large whales. Their sleek, shiny bodies porpoised across the sea's surface, and they remained with them for a couple of hours. Then, just as suddenly as they arrived, they left. Like synchronised swimmers, they took a deep breath and all dived down into the deep. And, as the Dall's porpoises were going down, other creatures were coming up, and where the two met there was another slaughter. The porpoises worked together to round up large congregations of Pacific hake and then tore into their tightly packed shoal. Soon, there was little left except the usual shimmering cloud of fish scales and oily fragments of flesh floating in the water.

Knucklehead and his mother were unaware of the drama playing out below them. They pressed on, entering Clarence Strait where they passed the remains of the steamship *Topeka* resting on the sea floor in 500 feet of water. It had struck West Devil's Rock on a foggy night in the summer of 1897. They passed Coffman Cove and its famous oyster beds on the northeast coast of Prince of Wales Island and swam by gill nets test-fishing for salmon in Chichagof Pass. This time Knucklehead stayed well clear.

The sky turned from gold to red to purple as tiny flecks chased long strands of dark grey clouds that seemed to hang in the breeze. They were small birds – blackpoll warblers – and they were on an extraordinary journey too. Others of their kind nest more usually in evergreen forests in the eastern half of

63

North America, but the species has expanded its range so much that now many are to be seen in the west. These western birds, however, follow the migration routes of their forebears, first heading up the east coast from South America, where they spend the winter in tropical forests in Brazil, before turning west to northwest Canada and Alaska. When science finally comes to analyse their flight plan, no doubt more records will be broken. For now, however, polarised light from the setting sun gave them the navigational information they needed to find their breeding sites further on.

The loud song of a northern water thrush burst from the edge of a bog close to the shore. It overwintered in tropical mangrove swamps in Central America, but here it was, breeding in Alaska, another tiny migrant that undertook an epic journey in order to breed in the insect-rich summer of Alaska. The urgent 'schwip, schwip' of a tree sparrow betrayed that he had arrived too. Overhead, a sharp-shinned hawk had a spat with another migrant raptor, a Swainson's hawk, the two birds performing outstanding aerobatics before flying on. The peaks of distant mountains were still dusted with snow, but summer was now well under way.

Forests lined the steep slopes, and in places spectacular waterfalls, like huge ribbons of silver lace, cascaded down between the trees. At one point, the shoreline had been eroded so badly that a house built on pilings was slowly collapsing. Already the south wing hung precariously over the rocks, and the front door opened onto a 20-foot drop into the sea. In Sitkine Strait, a huge raft with hundreds of floating logs was being towed to Coffman by a small tugboat, and in the opposite direction an enormous barge, loaded with row upon row of sea containers, chugged by. The whales avoided the ships and swam on. They had passed from Canadian into Alaskan waters. They did not have far to go.

The rocks along the shore blushed red and mauve in the evening glow, and Knucklehead and his mother reached the broad estuary of the Stikine River. As the tide rose it pushed western sandpipers further up the shore. They rooted along the mudflats, probing, turning seaweeds and stranded flotsam, searching for worms and other invertebrates, before they were covered at high tide. The birds had journeyed all the way from saltwater lagoons at Punta Banda on the Pacific coast of Baja, Mexico, taking short hops from one refuelling stop to the next – San Francisco Bay, Grays Harbour in Washington State, and the Fraser River delta, British Columbia, yet travelling 200 miles in a day at speeds approaching 45 miles per hour. They joined flocks of hardy rock sandpipers, sanderlings, surfbirds and dunlin that had been foraging there throughout the entire winter. Somehow, they were able to survive the short, dark days, seeking out ice-free zones amongst the rocks and estuaries. With a sudden shriek, the entire flock took to the air, hundreds of birds wheeling like a giant amorphous organism. Gradually they settled and then up they would go again, whirring this way and that, spooked now by the slightest unusual sound or movement. A fox – the likely cause of the panic – trotted nonchalantly along the shoreline, careful not to put a foot in the soft mud. The birds, their lengthening shadows forming grotesque dark shapes against the grey rock, used the sun's fading light to seek out safe roosting sites for the night. Offshore, the two whales took advantage of the quiet and rested, the first time for many days. They floated at the sea's surface, just the blowhole visible above the mirror-like surface. They were just off Rynda Island. The water was shallow here but deep enough for a sleeping whale.

It was still dark when they set off again, but as they headed towards Dry Strait, the water became alarmingly shallow. The strait floods twice each day, but in between times it is impassable. Ahead of them a salt marsh at the southwest corner of Farm Island marked the boundary of the land. The channel became narrower and shallower still, the strait having been filled with sediments brought down by the Stikine River. The main channel was uncertain and shifted almost daily, and the tidal range was no more than 16 or 17 feet at best. It was the flood tide, but would there be enough water for a giant whale to scrape through? Twice Knucklehead's mother had to flail against the muddy bottom, her great bulk preventing her from pushing forward. She could not go back. She could not turn. There was the serious danger that she would be left high and dry, and that meant certain death not only for the large female but for the calf too.

Inch by inch, the water rose and inch by inch the two whales eased themselves forwards. Then, the flood took them, pushing them through the strait and into deeper water. They followed the edge of the fluvial mud fan pushing out from the North Arm of the Stikine River and then took the channel to the east of Indian Point, which may account for them getting lost yet again.

In the morning they found themselves in a great, steep-sided fjord. Stands of old growth spruce and hemlock were juxtaposed with sheer rock cliff faces polished smooth by ice, and more spectacular waterfalls thundered into the deep, dark water.

The two whales hesitated; something was wrong. As they approached the head of the fjord they came close to the shore. Towering over them were huge, white jagged cliffs. The two whales hung motionless but alert, their long white flippers held out on each side and clearly visible even in murky water thick with plankton. They felt rather than heard a deep rumbling. The youngster quickly took his usual station just above and slightly to the right of his mother's blowhole. He felt safe there, and kept as close to her as he dare.

A startling, high-pitched screech cut through the sea and Knucklehead's mother suddenly sped away. Knucklehead was taken by surprise but quickly chased after her. Out of nowhere a powerful surge hit him from behind and he tumbled through the water. The white crags were no ordinary cliffs – they were made of ice.

The whales had paused close to the mouth of a glacier and an enormous fragment had broken away. With an ear-splitting roar, the great slab slipped into the water, disappeared and reappeared, bobbing like a gigantic cork – four-fifths below the surface, one-fifth above. It displaced a huge wall of water that rolled across the sea and hit Knucklehead with tremendous force, tumbling him out of control. At the same time, another huge block of ice broke away from the base of the glacier – a 'shooter'. It rocketed to the surface, pushing into the air before settling back down.

In the churning eddies Knucklehead was completely disorientated. He swam down instead of up. The water was unusually deep here, almost 800 feet to the bottom. It was calm and quiet down there, but he was alone...quite alone. He called. It was more of a burp than a call, but there was no reply. He was lost and running out of air. He was just about to take a breath at the surface, when he was swamped by the great wave. Which way should he go, which way was 'up'?

Out of the gloom, a grey shape loomed towards him. It was a seal and it swam rapidly passed him, blood seeping from an injured flipper. It was in a hurry, and barely gave the young whale a second glance. Knucklehead turned to follow, but was stopped in his tracks. He was face to face with a shark, another large shark. Ever so slowly, it circled the baby whale. Knucklehead had seen many sharks before but this one was different again: there was something strange about its eyes.

It was a female Pacific sleeper shark, and her large rounded belly showed she was carrying pups. Ten growing embryos were lined up inside her body. A slice of energy-rich blubber from a young and defenceless humpback would certainly help them grow. With a wide, tooth-filled gape, the shark could do much harm. But it was the eyes, not the ominous mouth, that hypnotised the frightened whale.

She had parasites clinging to her eyes, and those parasites had even smaller organisms inside – luminous bacteria – so her eyes appeared to glow in the dark. Their eerie green light attracted fish to within grabbing distance of the shark's mouth, but now it mesmerised the baby whale.

Knucklehead remained still, careful not to give the predator a reason to attack. The shark's strange, unblinking eyes stared in the gloom. It tightened its circle, preparing itself for that first exploratory bite. The young whale's lungs were about to burst – should he flee? Suddenly, the great dark shape of his mother appeared out of the darkness. With a loud moan she manoeuvred her vast bulk between Knucklehead and the shark. Using her great flippers like oars, she steered her knobbly snout broadsides into its body. The shark tried to avoid the clash but the whale smashed against its side. It shook violently, but wriggled past the whale's huge body and dived as fast as its short, blunt tail would propel it. It disappeared into the depths.

Sensing Knucklehead's distress, his mother nudged his body and struck out for the surface. Awakened from his trance the young whale followed rapidly, swimming for all he was worth towards the bright, silvery ceiling above. He exploded from the surface, the fleshy ridges of his blowholes opening wide, sending a fountain of mucus and seawater high into the sky. He sucked in a life-giving lungful of air and gently lowered his head below the surface. He was safe.

The great wave had passed and the water was calm once more. The two whales doubled back. They moved slowly, not with deep dives but by gliding close to the sea's surface. Their heads rose out regularly. They blew, breathed and dipped below once more. Behind them floated the great slab of ice that had broken free from the glacier. It towered 100 feet above the sea, while hidden below the water was the greater part of its bulk.

The ice had been part of the LeConte Glacier at the southern end of the Stikine Icefield, the southernmost tidewater glacier in the northern hemisphere. Nourished by snow falling upon compacted snow 100,000 years ago, this particular slab of ice has ever so slowly bumped and scraped its way across Alaska's bedrock, edging towards the west coast at just a few inches a year. It has been part of a glacial tongue that has gouged a deep scar in the planet. Locked up in its deep layers are the secrets of the past, a continuous record of events on Earth from a time when woolly mammoths roamed the north to the present day when the poisons of industry and agriculture have been dumped from the atmosphere and trapped in the ice. A segment of this natural archive had been disgorged into the sea – a new calf…not a whale, but an iceberg.

The glaciers are vital to this place. They bring down sediment from the land and deposit it on the bottom of the sea. Offshore winds and strong currents cause upwellings that drag up nutrients from the seabed to the surface where they feed algal blooms in spring and summer, and then so on up the food chain – from the floating larvae of crabs and lobsters, through small fish and then larger fish to seals and killer whales.

Knucklehead and his mother swam through a strange world of floating ice. All around them icebergs drifted in the slow-moving current. Some were the size of cathedrals, carved by the sea into fantastic shapes – deep blue caverns, grey arches, and ice cliffs tinged green by algae. Their flanks were streaked with layers of silt and stones that their mother glaciers had scraped from the land. Their surfaces glowed soft pink and orange and purple, taking the colour of the sun and squeezing its dying rays between the tiny, tightly packed crystals of ice.

Down their sides, ribbons of melted water fell into cracks, and pockets of aquamarine trickled into the sea many feet below. The heavier freshwater emptied into the lighter saltwater, driving an upwelling of nutrients around the margins of the berg. Ice-shrimps crowded the less saline water around the submerged base and were food for small fish which darted in and out of the iceberg's shadow. A party of juvenile harbour seals and a noisy gaggle of gulls chased the schools of young sablefish and juvenile walleye pollack that concentrated in the unexpected area of plenty.

It did not seem long before another day was drawing to a close. Low on the horizon the setting sun reflected off the gently undulating surface, giving the water the colour and texture of liquid gold. Storm petrels danced stiff-legged on the sea, their twilight ballet sending hundreds of tiny concentric ripples across its surface.

Closer to shore a violet, undulating shadow appeared just below the surface. It was a gigantic school of small fish – herring – and as the millions of glittering bodies rose from the depths, the pressure on their frail bodies reduced and air escaped from a million tiny swim bladders, the cloud of air bubbles causing the sea to boil and roar. There were so many herring a person could almost walk on the water. The fish were there to spawn. As they rolled and squirmed, each female shed tens of thousands of eggs, while the males, motivated by movement and flashing scales, produced milky clouds of pale milt. As male and female fragments met and fused, the eggs sank slowly to the bottom, sticking to rocks, shellfish, seaweeds, in fact anything below the glutinous deluge. Their annual duty done, the adult fish swam on, leaving their countless offspring to grow and develop alone and unprotected. By producing many, some might survive. But the frantic activity and the effervescing sea had already attracted unwelcome attention.

A high-pitched piping announced the arrival of the best part of a thousand harlequin ducks, colourful birds decked out in the black, white and red patchwork pattern of their namesake. They swooped down, feeding eagerly on the feast of silvery caviar. The ducks were on their way inland, to white-water rivers where they breed, but for now they took what the sea provided.

On the high peak of a melting berg, a bald eagle stood regally, casting his wary eye over his domain. It was the highest vantage point on the sea. Unperturbed, a pair of male Barrow's goldeneye were out to attract the ladies. Decked out in their Sunday best black-and-white plumage, they flapped uncomfortably into the air, but once airborne, they shot across the fjord at extraordinary speed.

On a large pancake-shaped slab of floating ice the last of the harbour seal mothers prepared her offspring for a precarious life at sea. The seals migrated here each spring to drop their pups on the ice floes that break away from glacial cliffs. They were safe there from both land and sea predators. She had given birth to her big-eyed pup, already in its adult coat, and then suckled it and weaned it in the space of just three weeks. The two slipped silently into the dark waters and were gone.

A Kittlitz's murrelet, diving for Pacific sand lance, bobbed back to the surface and took off – the last dive of the day. It was heading to its bare, rocky nest site 50 miles inland. The sky above blended into twilight, the sun dipping below the northwestern horizon. But this is nearly the land of the midnight sun; by midsummer it almost fails to set at all: 18 hours of sunlight, 18 hours of feeding but 24 hours of danger. In late spring and early summer, the dark night comes only briefly to these latitudes.

As dusk approached the two whales had reached The

Brothers, a string of rocky islets and local meeting place for a band of noisy male sea lions. They belched, barked and jostled each other, waiting for who knows what.

Without warning Knucklehead's mother dived below, then swam rapidly to the surface, bursting from the water. Three-quarters of her vast bulk hung momentarily in the air and time stood still until she turned on her side and crashed back down in a mountain of spray. In the distance she had heard the splash of another whale breaching, and this was her reply.

In the fading light another whale, and then another, splashed its signature. Like a roll call, each whale in the area was announcing its presence and position. The group from which they had become separated were not far away. They had caught up, and for the first time in his life Knucklehead was approaching his mother's summer feeding grounds. She breached again, and again – five times 30 tons of blubber, muscle and bones burst from the surface, twisted in the air and plunged back into the sea. It was as if she was pleased...as if all the whales were pleased, to be together again.

Knucklehead and his mother approached the other whales. It was still dark, the kind of stillness and darkness so characteristic of Inside Passage, but it was not silent. The sonorous moans of the scattered herd filled the sea with sound, while the sky above was illuminated with sudden flashes of light. As Knucklehead came to the surface to breathe he saw waving curtains of incandescent colour rippling across the night sky. It was the Aurora Borealis – the northern lights, a spectacular natural display taking place 200 miles above the Earth's surface. The ghostly veil sparkled whitish green, then pink, and its bottom edge glowed crimson. On that short summer night the aurora was brief, delayed by a sun reluctant to set and chased away by the light of a new day. For the whales the brief hours of darkness passed uneventfully.

CHAPTER FIVE
ALEXANDER ARCHIPELAGO

The early morning sun wrenched itself free from the far-off horizon and climbed effortlessly into a clear, blue sky. It warmed the rocks stained red, brown, green, yellow, orange and black by lichens. Some were simple ground-hugging encrustations, while others had leaf-like lobes or feathery spikes. Wild flowers, including the yellow flowers of silverweed, carpeted the ground between stands of spruce and cedar. Its roots, which taste like parsnip, were once a staple food of the local people. Nagoonberry, lupine, and fireweed were all in flower, as was Alaska's state flower, the forget-me-not. A yellow-rumped warbler hopped across the rocks at the water's edge. It was searching for insects and other small creatures. It was the one of the last bird migrants to leave last autumn and first to arrive this spring. As the tide ebbed, a large violet starfish was left high and dry, draped over a seaweed-encrusted rock. It attracted the unwelcome attention of a noisy gaggle of laughing gulls.

A crowd of Arctic terns had just arrived from their epic migration from the southern hemisphere, a journey of over 12,000 miles. By living at both ends of the world they benefited from more hours of daylight than any other bird in the world. A male plunged into the sea's glassy surface and emerged with a small silvery fish in his bill. He flew directly to his new partner who was watching from a wooden piling and offered her his catch. She accepted, delicately taking the fish and deftly swallowing it whole. They would soon be brooding eggs and raising the next generation of Alaska's Arctic terns.

Against the dramatic background of mountains still with snowy peaks, a bald eagle cried out from its perch on a dead tree, flapped unhurriedly into the air and glided nonchalantly along the shoreline. It was being harassed by a handful of worried ravens, but it paid no heed. They had nests nearby and saw the eagle as a threat. They called occasionally, their deep croaking 'kronk, kronk, kronk' echoing around the wooded islets.

In the silences, the blows of whales could be clearly heard across the bay, and the incessant barking of sea lions carried from a distant rookery. A small group of Dall's porpoise crossed the channel leading to the open ocean. During the night they had joined a bigger pod of nearly 200 and they had rounded up lanternfish out at sea. Now, they had split into smaller daytime resting groups. They arched gracefully in and out of the water, their splashes clearly heard across the surface of a still and quite sea.

For Knucklehead's mother at last it was time to feed. This was the reason she had travelled all this way. That summer, the waters of southeast Alaska were rich in tiny living things. She had not eaten since she had left these feeding grounds six months ago, so she had to build up her fat reserves to survive the long fast of the following winter. She would be trying for a ton of food each day for the next three months.

The two new arrivals swam slowly through the flotilla of other whales, all eagerly fishing. A youngish male was lazily scooping in a cloud of krill, tiny shrimp-like creatures that swarmed in the plankton-filled waters. It turned on its side and launched itself across the surface with its mouth open. When it closed it again it had a mouthful of seawater and krill, an Alaskan bouillabaisse. Another whale, a large female, had her own novel technique. She pushed herself vertically out of the water so her body and flipper formed the shape of a cross and then sank back down. As she submerged she opened her mouth and, like bathwater going down a plughole, the seawater and krill rushed straight in. Then, she raised herself up again and let gravity ease the food down her throat.

Not far away, two humpbacks were working together. They lunged through the water, turning and scooping krill they had driven close to the surface. They moved in perfect harmony, like two synchronised swimmers. The first whale created a small area of upwelling that the second whale could take advantage of and both gained a mouthful of food. The krill was so thick the two humpbacks were taking 2,000 pounds a day.

Knucklehead's mother, however, was looking for a particular group of whales, one with which she fed every year. In Hawaii, whales tended to avoid each other, but here on the feeding grounds elite groups of whales cooperated. Knucklehead's mother was a long-time member of one of the best. She made for the Chatham Strait where the water was boiling with herring. These small fish had spent the winter in deeper waters where it did not freeze, and after spawning, they congregated in amazingly large numbers over shallow banks where they were feeding on tiny drifting animals – the young of starfishes, crabs, and other sea creatures. These hordes – the zooplankton – were themselves grazing the minuscule single-celled plants of the sea – the phytoplankton. With almost 24 hours of sunlight, their numbers increase phenomenally throughout the summer. Together all these creatures form a chain – a food chain – that ends with whales.

She spotted what she thought was her group, and headed straight for the nearest whale. They had located a mother lode. Whales around the fish breached and tail slapped. They were concentrating the fish and coordinating their movements at the same time. When she reached them she saw that that it was the right group, her group. Big Mama, a large, scarred and weather-beaten veteran, led the group, and she ruled it with a rod of iron. However, she was tolerant of mothers with calves, so several mothers were members of her group. Calves tended to get in the way, so Knucklehead had to watch from a short distance away, while his mother joined the other adult whales.

It was the first time he had really been away from his mother, so he made the best of his newly acquired freedom. He swam towards a forest of giant kelp and began to play, draping the fronds across his flippers, coming up for air, rolling and slapping his flippers on the surface. A floating log became a plaything. He nudged it with his snout, then pushed it below and watched it bob back up to the surface. He was not alone. The young female with the white flippers was here too, for she also had been sent to play. Her mother was part of the same feeding group as Knucklehead's mother. The two parents had avoided each other in Hawaii, but now they would work together.

Visibility was remarkably low. There was so much plankton in the water Knucklehead could barely see a couple of yards ahead. Small shoals of herring appeared and disappeared around him. He tried chasing them, but they were remarkably quick. It was a good game nonetheless. For his mother, however, events that were about to unfold were deadly serious. She had to maximise her chances of gathering food, and Big Mama's group were adept at doing just that.

More breaching was followed by more tail slaps, and then the 'team' – for that was what it was – were ready. There were 10 whales and each had its own place in the team and a specific role to play. One by one, the whales raised their flukes and dived below. One whale then began to blow bubbles from its blowhole, and as it blew, it began to spiral upwards. Slowly a huge shoal of herring was surrounded by a rising column of sparkling bubbles. The reflections panicked the fish and drove them into a seething aggregation at the centre of this 'bubblenet'. Another whale screamed an extremely loud feeding call, the frightful noise helping to scare the fish to the centre. Then, at another clearly audible trumpet-like signal, the entire group rose up through the core of the encircling bubbles and opened their mouths to engulf the struggling fish.

On the surface all that could be seen initially was an enormous ring of bursting bubbles. It was about 100 feet across. The sea hissed like bacon in a frying pan and small fish leaped in all directions. Gulls swooped in to grab what they could. And then with a great roar the whales burst out in a confusion of gaping mouths, wiry baleen and waving flippers like a gigantic, untidy flower opening on the surface of the sea. Team spirit broke down momentarily as the whales pushed and shoved. Many fish escaped, leaping or swimming for all they were worth. Many more were trapped. The grooved throat of each whale distended incredibly to form an enormous wobbly bag, like a gigantic accordion filled with seawater and fish. Then each whale used its enormous tongue to push the seawater out through the comb-like baleen that grew down from the pink-coloured roof of its mouth. The fish were trapped inside and after one enormous swallow the whales were ready to feed again. They raised their flukes and dived below.

Knucklehead moved across from his play area and managed to scoop up a few stunned herring, but for the moment he still fed mostly on his mother's milk. As the bubbles began to reach the surface he quickly withdrew, and only just in time. The entire team burst through the surface again, and they kept doing this time and again for the rest of the day, entire shoals of herring disappearing in one collective gulp.

In the krill-rich area across the channel, a solitary whale blew a bubblenet just five feet across. Maybe he was practising for his big day with a bubblenet team, but for the moment he had mastered the technique and was scooping in great mouthfuls of the tiny creatures.

Closer to the shore another group of humpbacks chanced upon a shoal of oil-rich euchalon or 'hooligans'. With such a density of fish the whales did not blow bubbles but instead swam along the surface in line abreast and lunged at the shoal with their mouths open wide. Their long white flippers were held out horizontally either side of the body and were clearly visible to the fish. All they saw, though, was a line of white bars separated by dark areas. Avoiding the white stripes the fish attempted to escape through the dark patch, and swam straight into the whales' mouths. It was hard to avoid being engulfed by a maw 15 feet wide. Few escaped, and those that did fell prey instead to flocks of gulls that clustered about the surface.

As far as the eye could see, the fine misty blows of 100 whales drifted in the air. All around, large and small groups of humpbacks littered the sea, feeding continuously and urgently over the shallow offshore banks where fish concentrated in huge numbers. One youngster, learning the many ways to gather food, managed to get his techniques thoroughly mixed up. He blew a cloud of bubbles, rose through it, beat his tail, dived, surfaced and then lunged horizontally with its mouth wide open…nevertheless he caught a few.

The more aggressive individuals herded the fish and stunned them by smashing their tail onto the water surface or by slapping their long, white flippers in such a way as to create tremendous splashes. Another whale adopted an even more ingenious method. It lay on its side with its mouth open and swam in a circle, thrashing all the while with its tail. The commotion collected fish into the centre of the spiral where the whale scooped them up with no trouble at all.

There were scoundrels here too. Even whale society has its crooks. While several hard-working individuals blew a large bubblenet, two others swam surreptitiously into the middle of the ring of rising bubbles and wolfed down the food before the bubble-blowers had had time to surface. Whatever the method, these whales had to put on as much fat as they could during the shortest time. They had only three frantic months to prepare for the return journey south.

Accompanying Knucklehead's mother's group were noisy flocks of seabirds, greedy opportunists ready to snatch anything that tried to escape. When their crops were full and they were almost too heavy to fly, they flopped back to their tatty nests perched precariously on high, rocky cliffs on the outer islands of the archipelago. They returned to land, either to share incubation duties with their partner or to feed a sordid concoction of regurgitated fish to their newly hatched chicks.

Each bird, depending on its species, returned to its own particular space on the cliff. They were like people returning to their own homes in a block of high-rise flats. They caught the updraft at the bottom of the cliff and rode the wind like passengers in a lift. Somehow, each one located its own nest and even heard and recognised the cries of its own chick. The number of birds nesting together was staggering; there were thousands of birds in a single seabird city or 'bazaar'. It was smelly, noisy and confusing, but there was order in the city, each species arranged according to its needs.

Closest to the water were the cormorants and shags. They made their scruffy nests of seaweed on the flat rocks above the high tide mark. Above them on narrow balconies sat razorbills and guillemots or murres. The guillemots had mottled eggs, each one with its own colour pattern for individual recognition. Still higher were the kittiwakes and fulmars with their seaweed and guano nests glued fast to even narrower ledges. Their eggs were pointed at one end only. If bumped accidentally they turned in a small circle and were less likely to roll off the cliff. At the top, gulls preferred the open vistas of the cliff-top plateau where their clumsy chicks could wander without fear of them falling over the side and they could see predators, such as jaegers and ravens, approaching from afar. The jaegers were merciless in their attacks, swooping on the city, alert to a mother bird's momentary carelessness. They scooped up screaming chicks and broke into unattended eggs, the parents helpless in their panic.

The colony, however, was more than a nesting site. It was refuge. All the birds built nests, laid eggs, hatched their chicks and fed their young at exactly the same time. There was safety in synchronised numbers. Even nest predators became sated. It was also an information centre. Birds knew where to find food by watching other birds. Incoming birds returned directly from feeding sites at sea, and the sitting birds spotted from which way they came. When it was their time to feed they headed out in the same direction. First they glided down to the sea's surface, bathed and preened, and then took off, some to the open sea, others to the whale feeding grounds. They left in their own time, in ones and twos, but a few miles from the nest site they joined with others to form small flocks of 20 or more. They travelled in lines or in V-formations, like ducks and geese but closer to the water. The leading bird periodically bobbed up to check the heading of incoming flocks, corrected its course and the others followed. Some located the whales and joined in the squabbling.

By midday, hundreds of seabirds were swarming onto a patch of sea just a few yards across. In the noisy brawl they extended their wings, each bird jostling its neighbours to retain its place in the crowd. They fought vigorously for anything that resembled food. Knucklehead surfaced just in time to see one bird take a small fish and then the others chase it and mob it mercilessly until it was forced to regurgitate its prize and have it stolen from under its nose. The others argued noisily until one was able to pluck up the scrap and fly away to a discreet distance, where it swallowed its ill-gotten gain undisturbed.

When the whales drove the shoals to the surface, the sea sizzled. Fish were leaping for safety in all directions and the birds simply dropped down to pick them off. Then with a mighty whoosh the whales burst through the surface. The birds flew up in panic, but one hapless soul was sucked into a gaping maw and was lost.

Suddenly, all the whales stopped feeding. They were alert and listening. Knucklehead was alarmed and swam rapidly to his mother's side. In the sudden quiet, he heard a distant cry. A large male humpback moved towards its source. He lifted his chin high and brought it crashing down onto the sea, the clap reverberating around the islands. It was sign of aggression, a chin slap performed to intimidate whatever was out there. The sounds became louder – squawks and then trains of clicks. The humpbacks became agitated. One, then two, spyhopped, raising their heads above the water, straining to see what was coming. And, there they were – more killer whales. Their distinctive black-and-white pattern and sword-like dorsal fins were unmistakeable. The fin of the large, 30-foot-long male pointed six feet straight up into the air. They were moving at speed, porpoising frequently to reduce drag by travelling part in the air and part underwater. Occasionally one leaped higher, crashing back down in a breach.

The humpback cows and calves gathered together into a large group, but the young white-flippered female was not with them. Her mother lifted the front part of her body clear of the water and searched around desperately; then she spotted her. The youngster was still playing near the kelp, unaware of the danger. Her mother sank back down, turned sharply, and raced towards her. The killers where close and gaining fast. She would have to fight it out alone.

Unaccompanied cows and bulls turned and tail slapped. Knucklehead pushed closer to his mother. He was a big boy now, but he still sought her protection. She, in turn, placed herself between him and the newcomers. They were so close their calls were ear-splitting. They raced in amongst the humpbacks, but did not stop. They kept on going. They were not interested in whales; they were chasing salmon.

The orcas were a resident pod, and part of the Alexander Archipelago was their patch. Unlike the nomadic transient pods that had a predilection for the meat and blubber of seals and sea lions, and the occasional whale calf, these characters liked fish. They herded them like sheepdogs with sheep. They fanned out in a semicircle and pushed the salmon towards the shore. A huge sheer wall of granite about a half-mile long was ahead of them and the orcas kept pressing forward. In a mad panic, the salmon leapt clear of the water and slammed into the rock. Salmon were everywhere – in the water, in the air, and sliding down the granite, having knocked themselves out. The dorsal fins of the orcas cut cleanly through the water as they picked off the fish. Having eaten their fill, they swam silently away, leaving chaos in their wake. The group of Dall's porpoises had slipped in and were cleaning up. They often followed resident orcas, picking up scraps from the killer's table. A bald eagle swooped in and grabbed a choice specimen in its powerful talons. It flapped hard with its heavy load, and made for a flat-topped rock where it tucked into the firm pink flesh.

The orca foraging party consisted entirely of females and juveniles. The huge bull had not taken part. His tall dorsal fin caught the afternoon sun as he patrolled a half-mile out to sea. He ensured that nothing untoward happened to his group. He was not their leader, for one of the older females led the pod, but he was their guardian.

If whales could breathe a collective sigh of relief, the humpbacks did then. The large group split up, each whale or small group of whales going their own separate way. Feeding continued – day *and* night. The pitch darkness of summer nights was short-lived, but with every second having to count, bouts of frantic activity were punctuated by very brief periods of rest. Knucklehead's mother continued to feed in the dark, but adopted yet another technique. She emitted clicks and buzzes, dubbed 'megapclicks' (from the species' scientific name *Megaptera norvaeangliae*) by the listening scientists. The sounds were remarkably similar to the echolocation signals used by dolphins and killer whales, but whether they really were echolocation sounds was yet to be determined. They could have been communication sounds with another whale or 'startling' sounds to herd fish. However, she made sharp body rolls that coincided with each click series, and these ended with a 'terminal buzz', indicating perhaps that she had located shoals of herring or krill and had turned on her side to engulf them. In this way, she was able to feed in the dark.

She could use sounds in this way because her brain was specialised to process sound. The ratio of her brain size to body size was low compared, say, to a dolphin's, but her brain was nevertheless large and convoluted. The cerebral cortex – the part of the brain where thought processes occur – was similar in complexity to that of dolphins. Groups of her brain cells were organised into 'islands', an adaptation to promote the rapid exchange between neurons. Humpbacks might be brighter than we think, at least in the sound domain, and that night Knucklehead's mother was showing it.

At sunrise, a brief lull in feeding prompted one whale to drift off to sleep. It lay, just like a log, on the surface. The inactivity was infectious. Another became still…and another…and another, until all the whales had stopped feeding. It was the early morning siesta. Time to recharge their batteries from a frantic night's fishing. All that could be heard was the occasional blow. The air was still, and the spray hung fleetingly above each breather.

A sea mist pushed in from the ocean. First just wisps floated close to the flat calm water. The wisps then became strands and the strands turned into banks, and soon the sleeping whales were enveloped in a milky white fog. Visibility was down to 100 yards. Sounds were magnified. Just the hum of insects pervaded the air, but the drone became increasingly loud. It was not insects at all; it was a ship. A sudden blast from a foghorn brought the whales immediately out of their stupor. Not knowing which way was safe, they scattered in all directions. The ship had slowed and was carried along only by its forward momentum. The captain was aware of the whales ahead and was trying to avoid them. The ship slowed almost to a stop. It crept forward. The foghorn sounded again. Most of the whales were clear. It inched forward some more. The cavitation caused by a faulty propeller could be heard clearly, yet for some inexplicable reason a young male humpback moved not away from but towards the ship at the moment its propeller came into view. It tried to dive but the blade clipped its dorsal fin and part was sliced away. Blood poured into the water, but the damage was minimal. It would heal. The whale was lucky not to have lost its life; it was a narrow escape. The ship moved quietly on.

*   *   *

By late summer, the herring had either been fished out of near-shore waters or they had moved into the deeper parts of the sea. A few patches remained and the humpbacks vied with other creatures – seabirds and seals – for the last mouthfuls. Knucklehead's mother abandoned group feeding and went in search of her own feeding site. She went first to a channel that led out to the ocean. Knucklehead remained close. She dived below and then with an explosive whoosh she surfaced. She was diving over a bank of mud, and close to the seabed there was a large congregation of krill. At the surface she rested and caught her breath, travelling along the surface in a series of slow, shallow dives. Then, gracefully and slowly she bent the rear part of her body almost double, raised her huge tail flukes clear of the water and slid gently down to the seabed. Knucklehead followed her down.

In a crevice in the rocks nearby another hard-working mother busied about her new offspring...all 30,000 of them! She first locked herself away with her enormous family on the same day that Knucklehead arrived in Alaska, but many weeks later they were still eggs, the cold water temperature causing their slow development. It meant that their mother, a Pacific giant octopus, was confined with them and would still be there until well into the autumn. She cleaned and aerated her eggs with extraordinary devotion, guarding them closely from anything that might do them harm. During the entire period she would not have fed. When the youngsters eventually hatched out and joined the rest of the floating larvae that grew up on these shores, her task was completed and she was spent. She was just five years old when she died.

Not far away, the father was going about his business as usual, indifferent to his developing offspring. He was interested only in food and he crept out of his hideaway on all eight limbs and jetted across the mud and onto another rocky outcrop, where he dropped onto a crab. He dwarfed the crab. He was a true giant. His sucker-lined arms spanned 20 feet, and he simply engulfed the unfortunate creature. It struggled at first, the shape of its arms and legs pushing out the webbing between the octopus's arms. Then, with extraordinary dexterity, the octopus pulled off its limbs, including the claws, and took the rest of the crab apart using its bird-like beak.

The seabed was crawling with life. A tiny but colourful male grunt sculpin crawled across the sand on his pectoral fin rays and hid in the shell of a giant barnacle. He had been guarding his eggs in a chimney sponge, but now they had hatched and his youngsters were at the mercy of the currents. Deeper down, sea slugs the size of footballs meandered through a forest of red and orange sea pens, and a sinister wolf eel chewed on a brown sea cucumber it had caught. A large and baleful ling cod hovered by a rocky outcrop already occupied by a bright red vermilion rockfish, and an disorderly pile of sunstars was feeding on each other. A pink, scale-less, naked-skinned, tadpole-like snailfish adhered by its sucker-like pectoral fins to a rock before breaking loose and feeding on worms and other bottom dwellers in the seabed sediments. They were just a few of the strange and wonderful marine creatures adapted to the brutal conditions on this northwest coast. They remained here, through thick and thin, when all around them was changing with the change of seasons.

Knucklehead and his mother meanwhile had surfaced, made three shallows dives and then dived deep again. Just below the surface they passed through a swarm of unusually large jellyfish. They had swarmed together in order to breed, hundreds of them progressing slowly to the west and the waning sun. Their large, brown, soft umbrellas pulsated slowly as they dragged bundles of long, colourful tentacles through the sea. Several amphipods – small lice-like crustaceans that flourished with them – sprawled across the broad bell of one giant nearly six feet across. The tiny hitchhikers were protected by the jellyfish's sting but outstayed their welcome by stealing scraps of its food. Sometimes they even turned to eating the jellyfish itself. Below the bell tiny fish darted amongst the tentacles, safe from predators and somehow protected from the rows of deadly stinging cells.

On the seabed, sea snails with iridescent shells sparkled like stars in the deep gloom. Scattered amongst them were bright red sea cucumbers with bunches of feathery tentacles. Soft corals, with their colourless stems tipped red, littered the sea floor. They sat alongside patches of light green sea anemones. Among these underwater gardens, see-through shrimps hovered motionless, while here and there female rock gunnels – eel-like relatives of the blenny family so common in seaside rock pools – coiled their bodies protectively around their small balls of eggs.

The whales reached the cloud of swarming krill and gulped in great mouthfuls of seawater and food. Then, all of a sudden, birds surrounded them. They were long-tailed ducks. Their black-and-white bodies were propelled through the water by short, powerful wingbeats. They flew underwater, weaving around the whales in search of wayward krill, which they grabbed delicately in their beaks.

By this time the two whales had drifted out on the ebb tide and into the ocean proper. At the surface Knucklehead was waiting patiently for his mother return when he spotted several grey whales. They were already heading to their winter courtship and calving sites in shallow lagoons at Baja, Mexico. They had been to the Barents Sea for the summer, where they had scraped amphipods and tubeworms from the mud. Wherever they had been feeding, they left behind long grooves across the soft sea floor, and these could even be seen from the air. Now, the first of the whales were heading south.

Overhead the ordered ranks of migrating geese families were flying to warmer climes, leaving the Arctic tundra where they had courted, nested and brought up their own young before the weather had turned. In the recognisable V-formation each bird flew in the turbulence caused by the wings of the bird in front, helping it to fly further for less energy. The leading bird changed from time to time so that all could benefit. Smaller birds passed by too, flying alone or in small groups. An Arctic tern flew over; its short, high-pitched 'kip' call indicating it was also ready to depart. It would be flying from one end of the globe to the other, seeking out the lands where the sun never sets and where the feeding is good. Remarkably though, this pigeon-sized seabird will somehow find its way back to the same breeding site next year, meet with the same partner and find a scrape in the sand that is their nest…and all this after a round trip of at least 24,000 miles.

At this time of the year all the animals of the north seemed to be on the move once more, this time escaping the shortening days, plummeting temperatures and shortage of food. The first flurries of snow had already settled on the mountains. For the residents, it was time to prepare for winter. A solitary grizzly walked the beach, searching for clams, while a mile or so inland a group of bears were staking out the rapids at a river narrows. Normally solitary figures, these bears were putting up with each other for their brief sojourn on the river. They need to fatten up, before retiring to their winter dens. They had fed well on the autumn berries, but now they needed some good solid food – Pacific salmon. The fish were returning to salmon redds in the headwaters of the rivers in which they were born. They had gone to sea two years ago, had grown fast in the ocean and were now were returning to breed.

The bears were spread out across the small waterfalls, waiting patiently for the salmon to leap. Some bears were so skilled they

In the seas off Maui, a calf balances on the snout of its mother while playing at the surface not long after it was born.

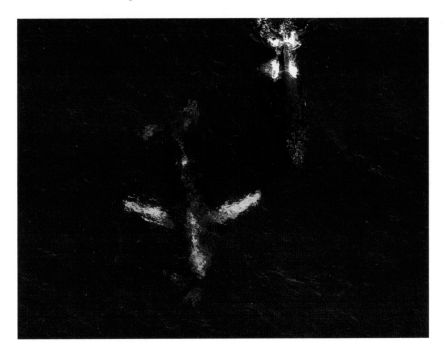

The long white pectoral fins of the humpback whale are clearly seen even from the air.

The sheltered bays on southern shores of Hawaii's islands are the maternity and nursery sites for humpback whales.

A female whale slaps her pectoral fin on the surface while being pursued by an army of bulls, all intent on being her escort.

Off southeast Alaska, a sleeping whale blows while breathing.

A humpback whale breaches some distance from a whale research boat in the Alexander Archipelago, southeast Alaska.

A young humpback calf copies its mother when learning how to breach.

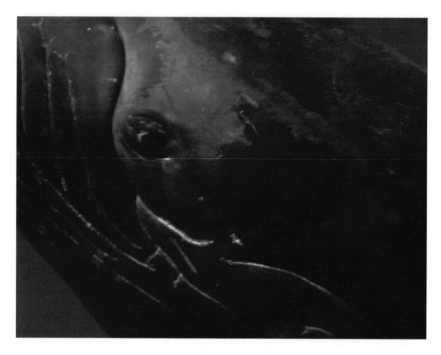

A humpback's eyes are at the side of its head so it cannot see directly ahead or behind.

Sharks are attracted to the afterbirth, but although these grey reef sharks may look menacing, they are not a serious threat to a newborn humpback whale.

A bull humpback blows bubbles from its mouth during a contest for the right to be primary escort to a female.

The bubbles blown from a bull humpback's mouth burst at the surface.

Below the surface a whale is blowing an individual bubblenet as it fishes for krill off southeast Alaska.

One individual in southeast Alaska has a unique way of fishing. It sinks vertically, mouth open, to catch fish, then rises vertically to swallow them.

Killer whales are the only predators that will take on a full-grown humpback whale, but this pod is unlikely to attack – they prefer fish, especially salmon.

A bull humpback, known as a 'breath-holder', hangs in the water about 30 feet below the surface, off Maui.

Early in the morning in late summer in southeast Alaska, the blows of humpback whales seem to hang in the air.

A baby whale rises to the surface to take a breath but does not venture far from its mother.

A humpback calf remains close to its mother, keeping station just above and to the side of her head.

Mother and baby humpbacks are shadowed by an escorting male.

A humpback lies on its side and is about to slap its long pectoral fin on the surface of the water.

A bull humpback emits a cloud of bubbles from his blowhole to deter rivals from usurping his position as the primary escort to the female and her calf.

A group of harbour seals are on the top of an ice flow, safe from marauding killer whales.

A harbour seal rests on a block of ice that has calved from a glacier in the Alexander Archipelago.

Humpbacks surface like an untidy flower as they feed on a large shoal of herring using a bubblenet.

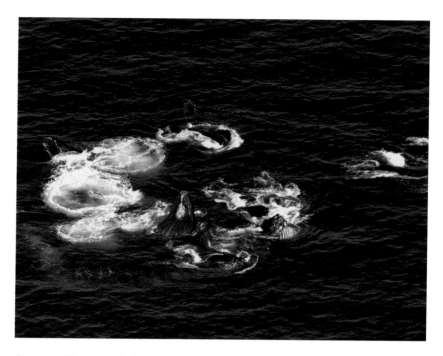

A group of humpbacks begin to surface through the centre of a circle of bubbles while bubblenet feeding for herring.

With its throat pleats expanded, and a mouthful of seawater and herring, a humpback surfaces during bubblenet fishing.

Markings on the underside of a humpback's tail flukes are like fingerprints, enabling whale scientists to recognise individual whales.

A humpback is about to slap its tail flukes onto the water surface; the sound of the impact is thought to be one way in which whales communicate.

A humpback calf looks small compared to its mother, but at birth it was already 16 ft long and weighed a couple of tons.

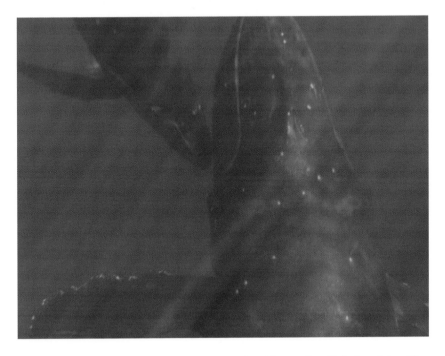

A baby humpback swims to its mother's underside to take thick, fat-rich milk from one of her teats.

An inquisitive young whale appears to dance as it swims to check out the photographer.

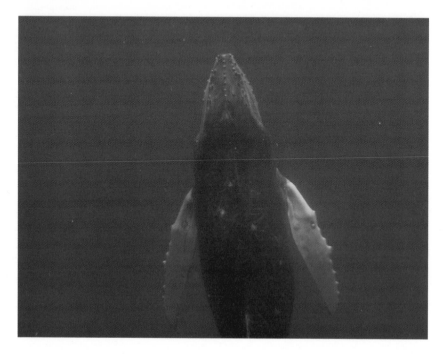

This young humpback has white pigment on the topside and underside of its long pectoral fins.

caught the salmon in mid-air; others plunged into pools and creeks and caught them underwater. After making a catch they stripped off the skin and feasted enthusiastically on the rich red or pink flesh and the body cavity filled with roe. Such was their eagerness to catch more fish they discarded half-eaten meals. Bald eagles, always on the lookout for an easy catch, dropped in to clear up their untidiness.

Occasionally tempers were lost and bears came to blows. The largest individuals occupied the best fishing beats, and they also did the most thieving. One bear caught a salmon, ran some distance away from the river to eat his food in peace, only to have it stolen by a larger bear. Size was everything in grizzly society. Smaller bears gave way to larger bears, whether males or females.

A bear fishing away from the main party waited patiently by a small pool and when a salmon chanced by it deftly hooked it onto the bank. A youngster possessed less finesse. It simply plunged into the water, the belly flop sending water and salmon flying. Others swam about with their heads under the water, catching fish when they swam too close. An enterprising individual stood on its hind legs and waded into the water like a bather trying not to get their costume wet. But when a salmon brushed passed its legs it reacted like lightning, hooking its prey with its large and powerful claws. A mother with three growing cubs fished apart from the others. As soon as she caught a fish, the youngsters squabbled over who should have the choice piece.

After an hour or so of intense fishing and feeding, the bears ambled off to rest and digest their meals. Others, further down the pecking order, arrived to take their place, but when the big boys came back the fur flew. The bigger bears chased the smaller ones away and had all the fishing to themselves. They gorged on the salmon and their protein-rich eggs. The experts amongst them were catching upwards of 20 fish in an hour.

In late autumn, when the salmon runs end, the bears would be gone. They would not be hibernating as such, but finding a cosy den and shutting down temporarily until spring. In the meantime, a red fox darted out of the forest, nimbly avoided any bears, grabbed a discarded fish and disappeared once again amongst the trees.

Out at sea, the two whales were also preparing for a coming change. It would soon be time for them to join all the other migrants heading south, but for now there were the last few mouthfuls of krill.

CHAPTER SIX
KILLERS!

The early light brought an early autumn storm. The warmer temperatures of late summer meant that the atmosphere held more moisture at this time of year. It was the rainiest season in southeast Alaska. But now the temperature had dropped suddenly. An icy cold wind blew in from the northwest, whipping up the sea into row upon row of foaming white horses. Lightning lit up the dark clouds, and the booming thunder seemed to shake the very Earth itself. A waterspout appeared on the horizon but died before it reached the land. Bird migrants delayed their journeys and set down to shelter from the squalls. They huddled, feathers ruffled against the sudden cold, with beaks pointing into the wind. Winter snow was blown haphazardly onto distant mountains, and the first flecks had been falling right down at the water's edge. It was water, though, not snow that was feared. On long sections of the coast, a storm surge had pushed into low-lying areas and had caused considerable damage. When the flood tide reached its zenith sections of coast were washed into the ocean, along with buildings and roads.

Storm or no storm, life had to go on, and the frantic need to feed up before winter proper set in was an incentive to be out in such inclement weather. Amongst the rocks and tufts of grass on a knoll above the shoreline, tiny inquisitive heads popped out from behind boulders and peered out of cracks. They were voles. Their numbers had been building in previous seasons and this summer they reached their peak. Predators were having a field day.

During a moment of calm, a vole broke cover and scuttled rapidly across an open patch of grass blown flat by the wind. A great grey shape swooped out of the sky and a loud yelp betrayed its identity. It was a jaeger or skua. Accelerating rapidly on a gust of wind, it swept down to attack, only to be confronted with a pair of very sharp teeth as the tiny rodent raised itself up on its hind legs to its full height and hissed and squeaked in protest. The bird swerved to avoid the toothy display and flew on, almost blown into a fallen bough by a sudden gust.

On the stony beach below, the mounting surf had thrown up the bloated carcass of a harbour seal. A large open wound on its side indicated it was the victim of a shark attack, probably a Pacific sleeper. These sharks were common in waters further to the north, often taking halibut from commercial fishing lines. Local fishermen tell of one occasion when a single skate of 100 long-line hooks brought up 67 sleeper sharks. They were once thought to be inveterate scavengers, but evidence like this dead seal suggested that they were skilled predators. In the Antarctic, French researchers had examined 36 sleeper sharks and in their stomach they had found the remains of colossal and giant squid, two formidable opponents. The sleeper was clearly more than a scavenger; it was one of the ocean's supreme predators, and here was the proof. A fox braved the icy wind and spray to take a bite, and the ubiquitous gulls, buffeted this way and that by the wind, dropped down to the beach for their share.

Out at sea a few humpbacks continued to fish. As they broke surface briefly to breathe they were almost invisible amongst white tops that were buffeted and fragmented into spume by the wind. Under the water the sound of the wind and the surf was dampened. Knucklehead was a baby no more; he was almost a yearling. He had doubled in length and increased his weight by eight times. Nevertheless, he still swam close to his mother. He followed her every move, occasionally catching his own fish and krill but still taking an occasional squirt of mother's milk. He manoeuvred himself under her body and probed for the mammary slit, drinking a jet of thick, pink-tinged liquid before returning to his swimming station. It would not be long, however, before he was fully weaned.

For the moment, he and his mother made the best of what krill and herring were left. They were just two of a handful of whales still on the feeding grounds, but conditions were becoming bleak and uninviting. It was time to move on. They turned to the southwest and headed out to the open ocean. They passed a group of whales still feeding. It was the white-flippered female and her mother, along with a group of whales without offspring. The mother heaved herself into the air, breaching in a cascade of spray that was blown by a violent gust of wind. It was if the whale was saying 'goodbye and safe journey'. The two migrants swam slowly past, one moment high on a wave, the next deep in trough. Then, as if playing in the waves, some whales started to breach more frequently, but there was more urgency in their behaviour than there had been before. They had heard a distant scream, not the calls of a harmless resident killer whale pod, but the unmistakeable cry of transients...potential whale killers. The calls stopped abruptly; they had started to hunt.

The humpbacks leaped and crashed continuously. One raised its head vertically out of the water – spyhopping – looking nervously through the wind-blown spray for the black-and-white whales. Using their huge flippers and powerful tails as makeshift weapons, they would make a stand. Two whales started to head lunge, crashing their chins against the waves. The other whales tried to gather into an untidy group as they did before. The orcas were still some distance away, but they knew exactly where the whales were located and in what formation. They swam slowly and menacingly side by side in a military line abreast, the huge straight dorsal fin of the large bull clearly visible between the waves and troughs of the turbulent sea. Several smaller curved fins, those of females and immature males, betrayed a pod of more than a dozen animals. After another brief exchange of calls they went silent again and, almost as one, they quickened their pace.

The humpback whales were noticeably and understandably nervous. Knucklehead swam alongside his mother. He was one of the youngest and most vulnerable members of the group. The adults drifted around waiting for the inevitable attack. The orca pod was getting closer. Then, quite unexpectedly, it split up. The large male together with a couple of females turned to the right and the others teamed up and swam off to the left. Then a third group headed straight for the core of the humpback herd. They remained ominously silent; the splashes of white on either flank a clear indication to each pod member where its neighbour was stationed. The humpbacks swam to and fro, emitting the occasional moan…waiting. Knucklehead's mother placed herself between Knucklehead and the approaching killers.

In a sudden burst of speed, one group attacked its first target – a solitary humpback bull. The great whale turned its belly towards the attackers and thrashed at them with its flukes. The powerful tail crashed down on the leading orca and it stood off bruised and battered but not about to give up. The humpback rolled and emitted a loud, wheezing blow under the water. The other orcas nipped at his body, tearing small chunks of blubber, but with another rotation and a great crash of the flukes they too were seen off and they swam away to regroup.

Knucklehead was terrified. The large orca male had spotted him hiding behind his mother and was swimming towards him, intent on an easy kill. It was smaller than the young humpback, but its wide mouth was filled with large peg-like teeth, not baleen. Knucklehead's mother twisted her body to fend off the killer with her long, white pectoral fins. The orca squirmed around her and seized Knucklehead by the tail fluke. Knucklehead thrashed for all he was worth. The predator's teeth lost their grip and scraped across the tail to leave what would become a permanent scar. The cow turned once more, her agility in the water far superior to that of the orca. She caught him with a mighty 'thwack' and the orca abandoned his assault on the calf, but he was not quick enough. Another humpback cow, seeing the attack, swam straight for the raider. She swung her massive chin, lined with rows of sharp-edged barnacles, like a gigantic knuckleduster, and slammed it into the male orca's body. The blow caught him amidships and he was almost carried clear of the water. He retreated.

The rest of the humpbacks were pursued mercilessly by the other orcas as they probed and tested. The great whales manoeuvred their enormous bodies almost nonchalantly, but effectively. Some were bloodied but none had yet succumbed to the onslaught. One had a slice taken out of its dorsal fin, while another had a gash along its lower jaw. The sea surface was littered with small chunks of blubber and skin, attracting gulls and other seabirds.

The skirmishes continued relentlessly, the humpbacks wheezing and moaning, the orcas clicking frantically and now screaming loudly. The larger whales were in small clusters of two or four animals, a gap of about 100 yards between them. The young female with white flippers was with her mother on the edge of the group. They seemed to be outside the danger zone. The killers pressed into the middle of the herd. In making these furtive attacks, they appeared to be testing the larger whales, looking for weaknesses, illness or the disabilities of old age. They attacked and harassed again and again, without rest. After several hours, the entire pod reformed and focused its attention on a single group of humpbacks. They had identified their target. They were heading towards Knucklehead's group.

All 12 adult orcas – three males and nine females – and their offspring formed into a crescent-shaped battle formation and swam rapidly towards their chosen targets. There was Knucklehead, his mother and two other cows, one a young female yet to breed and the other a much older female – the whale who had packed the punch which saved young Knucklehead earlier in the day. They sensed they were the quarry and swam faster, Knucklehead staying close to his mother as if joined by an invisible cord. The other whales swam unusually close to each other too, no more than five yards apart.

The orcas, calling out in loud and strident whistles and screams, seemed to respond to instructions from the oldest female in the pod. They spread out around the whales, easily overhauling the slower-swimming humpbacks. Knucklehead was close to the surface, swimming as fast as his flukes would propel him. His mother was directly underneath, her body a shield from any attacks from below. The other cows swam to the side and slightly below and behind. Two orcas dived below the group to start closing the trap. At this point the old cow suddenly turned, using her great pectoral flippers to twist her body, and aimed straight for the attackers. Startled by the sudden change of direction, the orcas scattered in all directions, regrouped and began to bait the old whale. Knucklehead swam on. The orcas had selected their victim. They moved in for the kill.

Four orcas flanked the old humpback as if herding it like a farm animal. They porpoised energetically through the waves, splashing and blowing, their black-and-white markings clearly visible each time they left the water. Two more swam below, preventing her from diving. The others, led by the large bulls, snapped at flippers and flukes like demented wolves. Her tail flukes were already badly shredded, weakening her ability to swim at all. A large orca rushed in and seized the small dorsal fin, ripping it away from the body in one smooth, unhurried movement. Blood poured from the great gash and stained the sea red. Greatly weakened by the injuries and exhausted by the chase, the humpback slowed considerably. Several of her assailants rushed at her failing body, leaping from the water and crashing into her back, while another swam over her blowhole preventing the old whale from breathing. Sensing the end was near, the two orcas below her belly swam up and stripped away chunks of blubber from under her chin. Another bit into the thinnest part of the tail, severing nerves, muscles and blood vessels.

Unable to move her tired, ragged tail, the old whale stopped swimming. The weight of killers around her head prevented her from reaching the surface. In a short while she drowned, turned belly-side-up and sank slowly to the bottom. Could it be that she had made the ultimate sacrifice for the rest of the herd? The old whale had led the orcas into relatively shallow water. In ones and twos they dived down and tore away the blubber of the lower jaw. They were after the ultimate delicacy – the whale's huge tongue.

But in the rush to escape, Knucklehead had become separated from his mother. She was nowhere to be seen. He surfaced, pushed his body out of the water as he had seen other whales do, and looked around. There were no whale blows, nothing, just wind-blown spume trailing across an angry sea.

There was no reassuring touch from his mother's flipper, no comforting sound, just the roar of the wind and waves. He was alone. He stopped swimming, not knowing what to do next. He hung in the water close to the surface, bobbing about like a cork. The light was fading. It was evening, and he was about to spend the night by himself in the Pacific Ocean.

* * *

The darkness fell with unbelievable speed. It was very different from the long days and short nights of summer, but the usual crowd of deep-sea creatures appeared around him all the same. They rose up from the depths – jellyfish, comb jellies, krill, small fish and tiny sharks, as well as the larvae of fishes, molluscs and crustaceans. It was as if the entire sea had suddenly come alive, and had come to greet the young whale. A school of small squid flew past, followed by a group of dolphins. They clicked and buzzed, using their echolocation system to keep track of their speedy prey. Dolphin sonar probably evolved for just such a pursuit, for squid come closer to the surface at night, making it easier for dolphins to catch them. But they were not alone. A bull sperm whale appeared. It was monstrous. At 60 feet long, it dwarfed Knucklehead. It took a breath, arched its back and was gone, disappearing deep into the inky depths.

Knucklehead was mesmerised, but he quickly snapped out of his daze. He had to do something. Instinctively, he turned to the south and began to swim. After no more than a few minutes, the sperm whale appeared again. It surged out of the water, its square head covered with the body and flailing arms of a giant squid. Knucklehead stopped dead in his tracks. The squid had planted the suckers of its eight arms against the side of the whale's head, but its body was firmly locked in the whale's jaws. It was bright red in colour and emitted startlingly bright flashes of blinding white. The two rolled over, submerged and then burst through the surface again. The squid's body was at least 16 feet long, and its two enormous tentacles were a further 20 feet long. They waved vaguely in the air before the two adversaries plunged back below the surface. Time and again they appeared and disappeared, until with an enormous slurp half of the squid's body broke away and disappeared down the whale's throat. The rest sank back into the depths. The whale dived and was gone, to be replaced by an entire pod.

Each of the whales broke through the surface with explosive blasts from their blowholes. They were cows, some with calves, and they had been feeding on smaller varieties of squid deep down in the submarine canyon below. They wallowed at the surface, breathing less frenetically and prepared to dive again, but something stopped them in their tracks. The killer whales were back, and there were more than 30 of them this time. They had sensed the struggling bull whale and squid and homed in on the location immediately.

The whales formed their marguerite defence position, this time with the calves at the centre. The larger whales lifted their heads clear of the water, the sound of click traces clearly audible at the surface. The killers buzzed around, squealing and screaming, nipping at any piece of a whale they could grab. The sperm whales lashed out with their tails, but the killers were fast and highly manoeuvrable. The cows dashed in and took chunks out of the whale's tailstocks and flanks. They retreated, regrouped and then came in waves, four or five killers at a time, adopting a 'wound-and-withdraw' strategy to wear down the sperm whale pod. Even youngsters took part, swimming in with their mothers, taking a chunk of blubber and then retreating again.

A whale was forced out of the wall and the killers bit it mercilessly, but two other sperm whales broke ranks and came to its rescue. One went on each flank and guided the injured whale back into the defensive formation. As Knucklehead hurried away, a small killer grabbed his tail fluke and bit hard. The young whale tried to escape but the smaller whale hung on tight. At the same time, one of the badly injured sperm whales rolled onto its side, near to death. A large bull killer whale came at it at full speed and slammed into its weakened body, pushing it sideways through the water. It grabbed a chunk of flesh and shook its head ferociously from side to side, then towed the carcass away into deeper water. Distracted momentarily, the smaller killer let go and Knucklehead swam for all he was worth, the rake marks on his tail flukes another permanent record of his close calls with killer whales. The lifeless body of the sperm whale floated to the surface, where it was battered by the waves, before being pulled below by the rest of the orca pod. The other killers took turns to take their slice of flesh. A slick of oil spread across the surface and was churned into froth. The rest of the sperm whales were badly injured, one with a great gash in its belly, its intestines draped across its back, and another with a great slab of blubber the size of a mattress dangling from its side. The orcas had disembowelled one and had been skinning the other alive. Few would survive their terrible wounds.

Knucklehead pressed on, lucky to be alive. Two mature humpbacks that had changed course to avoid the bloodbath passed close by. They were heading in the same general direction as Knucklehead, so he tagged along. They must be going to where he wanted to go, but little did he know that these whales were heading for Mexico and not Hawaii. Humpbacks also have breeding sites along the Baja Peninsula, and some of the Alaskan whales go there instead of Hawaii for the winter. If Knucklehead continued on this course, he would not be going home. In the meantime, he followed the two older whales for several days and nights. They, however, were stronger and faster, so eventually he tired, dropped back and had to watch them disappear over the horizon.

By this time the storm had abated and the sea was calm once more. Overhead, the sandhill cranes from Graham Island were on the way back to the Sacramento River. Their long, slender necks pointed forwards, their legs trailing behind. There were more birds now than when they went north, and they flew over in groups of three, parents flying with their new offspring. The family would remain together until they returned north next summer, the new generation learning the route and the ways of cranes from their elders. Unsuccessful breeders travelled in larger flocks, their wings beating almost in harmony, a slow downward beat followed by a quick upward flick. They were flying high, yet their incessant calling, a rolling 'kaar-roo', could be heard clearly at sea level.

Knucklehead dived, but instead of the familiar sea floor, the water seemed to go on forever. There was an eerie blackness below. The floor of the Pacific has just as varied topography as that on land. The deepest deeps and the highest mountains on Earth are in the sea, but directly below Knucklehead was a great chasm in the sea floor, the Astoria submarine canyon, the most westward extension of the Columbia river system. There were huge swarms of shrimps and krill along the canyon walls and the whale was able to feed properly for the first time in his life. Schools of hake, rockfish and yellowtail joined him, but he almost forgot to breathe. He raced for the surface, bursting through to take a vital lungful of air, and then he dived once more into the abyss to feed some more.

Far below him, on the floor of the canyon, large black sea lilies and basket stars opened like spidery flowers, and a vase sponge, like an upside down spinning top, pumped water through its intricate passageways. Pacific hagfish lay coiled like snakes, waiting for the dead or the dying to drop down from above, and a school of sablefish scoured the sea floor for food. A box crab scrambled across rocky cobbles, disturbing a Dover sole lying camouflaged on the sea floor, and fields of white sea cucumbers lay with their tentacles fully outstretched, filter feeding from the still, nutrient-rich waters.

Replenished, Knucklehead set off once again. As the walls of the canyon were left far behind, the near-shore waters became shallower. Forested shores gave way to sandy bays, then rocky headlands. On the sea floor canyons gave way to underwater plateaus and banks. Here the sea floor was littered with the egg masses of sea snails, each a yellow pinnacle of eggs. A ratfish glided over the bottom silt where a cold seep exuded methane on the seabed. It was a source of energy for bacteria that were the primary food for unusually large clams over six inches across. Where fluids flowed strongest grew mats of white filamentous bacteria. Bright red brittlestars were scattered like confetti across the ocean floor, and rocky outcrops were adorned with pricklebacks – small fish that rest on their pectoral fins and tail like miniature tripods.

The banks, bathed in the nutrient-rich waters of the California Current, attracted tens of thousands of Cassin's auklets and hundreds of black-footed albatrosses. The albatrosses had flown all the way from Knucklehead's homeland, from the low islands of Hawaii where they had nested to Hecetas Bank where they were feeding. There were also sooty shearwaters. They had made an even longer migration from New Zealand, in the southwestern corner of the Pacific. Pink-footed shearwaters and northern fulmars joined them in the feast, and so did Knucklehead. Small fish, shrimps and krill were still plentiful here, so the young whale could feed again. He was getting quite adept at rounding up small patches of krill or small fish. His mother had taught him well.

He began to notice other whales in the vicinity. They were feeding too, and they were humpbacks. He approached, moaned and whined, but they ignored him. They were too intent on feeding. A young whale was of no consequence to them. He left them reluctantly, and resumed his journey southwards alone.

After a day or so, he came to a huge swathe of kelp forests, similar to the kelp beds in which he had played on the feeding grounds. They were also similar to the forests on land; except the trees were seaweeds, and countless small gas-filled bladders held them aloft. Like tall straight boughs, the giant kelp stretched more than 100 feet from the seabed to the surface and the vital sunlight. They were anchored to the rocky bottom not with roots, but with thick, sturdy, finger-like holdfasts. An understorey of smaller red, brown or green seaweeds were scattered about their base.

With shards of sunlight beaming down between the fronds, the scene was not unlike a gigantic underwater cathedral and it teemed with life, a whole community of animals living in, on, under and amongst the kelp, different types of creatures occupying different layers in the forest. Nudibranchs or sea slugs and skeleton shrimps preferred the canopy at the surface, along with schools of blue rockfish that swayed with the surge of the waves that passed overhead. Strawberry-coloured sea anemones and orange cup corals were attached to the kelp stems – the stipes, and kaleidoscopic sea snails slithered up and down, rasping microscopic food from their surface. Swarms of mysid shrimps busied about the fronds, never straying far in case passing predators gobbled them up, while down below menacing wolf eels waited for the careless and the bold.

Kelp bass and rockfish swam in the understorey, chased by acrobatic harbour seals. A torpedo ray rested on the coralline-encrusted, rocky sea floor, ready to discharge a powerful electric shock – up to 220 volts – at anything foolish enough to take too close an interest. Brittlestars and turban snails hid amongst the strong, multi-branching root-like holdfasts, and battalions of sea urchins chewed on holdfasts, causing some fronds to break away in the autumn storms.

The giant kelp grows extraordinarily fast: up to 20 inches a day in spring, though in autumn the growth slows down. Bryozoans and tiny sessile coelenterates cover the fronds at this time of the year, like a dusting of winter snow. Knucklehead avoided the dense patches and swam along the edge of the forest. As he dived below he met a sea otter returning to the surface. It carried an abalone and two stones. When it reached the surface, it wrapped a frond of kelp around its body to prevent it drifting away, and floated on its back. Balancing one stone on its stomach it placed the abalone on top and then smashed at it with the other stone held in its forepaws – a hammer and anvil – extracting the juicy flesh, which it consumed eagerly before diving down to find some more.

As evening came, a school of senorita wrasses swooped onto the sandy seabed and buried themselves for the night. Above them kelp crabs, hanging tightly to the fronds, grabbed at anything remotely edible that floated past. Pipefish aligned their bodies with the kelp and disappeared from all but the keenest eyes. And as darkness fell, a small octopus emerged from a tangle of holdfasts and walked across the sand on its flexible arms. A nervous sanddab shifted position and swam off, breaking cover and giving itself away. It swam, though, in the wrong direction, right into the mouth of a sit-and-wait predator, a large cabezon, a giant species of sculpin.

On the sand flat adjacent to the forest, huge numbers of market squid appeared. They had jetted in from deeper water to spawn, a second peak of activity that followed another in early June. Males grabbed females, changing colour from

104

creamy white to fiery red, and held on as the pair dropped to the seabed and deposited 20 to 30 egg capsules, each capsule containing 200–300 eggs. As the night went on, large mounds began to accumulate and bat rays and angel sharks glided in to vacuum up as many eggs and squid as they could. Blue sharks arrived, swimming nonchalantly through the squirming squid, but gulping them down as fast as they could. Crabs and lobsters clambered through the pure white carpet and sea urchins shuffled in to feed on the scraps raining down from above. A sculpin swam off with its belly full and the tail end of a squid protruding from its mouth, and a blue shark fed voraciously on mating squid until sated, regurgitated its colossal meal and then started all over again. It was mayhem, not least because the squid mated and then died. Soon, there were fields of dying squid three or four feet deep.

Knucklehead's course meanwhile was taking him south along the Pacific coast of North America. The following morning was bright but overcast, the clouds high and the sea calm. He was relatively close to the shore, about a mile out, when up bobbed a whale calf. The young humpback stopped in his tracks. The calf was newly born. He was no more than 10 feet long. A short length of umbilical cord trailed from his belly and he had distinct folds – embryonic folds – along his side, right down to his tail. He was inquisitive. He came close to Knucklehead, touching him gently before circling. His mother then appeared – a grey whale. She remained a few yards away, protective and cautious. She eyed the young humpback suspiciously, and then she blew, breathed and sank below, circling the two young whales from a few feet below.

When he stopped, the calf's tail folded under and forward, probably the position it was in when he was in his mother's womb. It was still very flexible, bending upwards noticeably when he thrust down with his tail. All his movements were exaggerated and clumsy, and he could hardly hold his breath for more than a half a minute. He was barely an hour old, and everything around him was new. He went to his mother. He lay across her snout as she pushed him tenderly to the surface. He took a breath, turned and sprawled across her tail. Again she lifted him up, he took a breath and submerged. He went to Knucklehead several times more, touching him, slowly nudging him with his snout, but Knucklehead was now between the calf and his mother. She quickly intervened, swiping at the young humpback with her tail. He baulked and began to swim away. The calf followed for a few seconds but, at the sound of a loud blow from behind, he abandoned his new playmate and returned to his mother. She had given birth on the way south to Mexico; maybe she need not make the journey now.

Knucklehead, however, kept to his course, due south. Several more days and nights passed without event. Knucklehead was following the contours of the coast, but being too close to shore was about to get him into real trouble. He turned left when he should have turned right and passed unknowingly from the Pacific Ocean, under the Golden Gate Bridge and into San Francisco Bay. It was busy with boats, the mild autumn weather bringing out many weekend boat people. They were astonished to find themselves sailing along with a whale. Knucklehead ignored the spectators and continued on a line that was taking him increasingly further from the sea. He swam to the north of Alcatraz, passing a large black bat ray and a handful of small leopard sharks, and took a left around Angel Island, passing through the pillars of the roller-coaster-like Richmond–San Rafael Bridge. Western gulls and cormorants were roosting amongst its metalwork, while nearby a flight of pelicans headed out to sea in single file.

By late afternoon, Knucklehead had passed under the Carquinez Bridge and was off Benicia, by which time the

Solano County Sheriff's Department had been notified. They contacted the fisheries service of the National Oceanic and Atmospheric Administration (NOAA) who, in turn, arranged for whale biologists to take a look. By the time they arrived the light was fading, but they could still identify Knucklehead as a young humpback. Rio Vista coastguard ensured a 100 yard no-go area for small boats was maintained around the whale. The news, however, had got out and people were coming from miles around to see their new visitor. News helicopters were ordered to remain above a thousand feet lest they panic the youngster. But people on windsurfers whizzed around the whale and had to be moved on by the police. When night came, the crowds disappeared and Knucklehead was alone once more.

The following morning, Knucklehead's picture – or at least his back – appeared in newspapers and on television worldwide. He had become a celebrity. They nicknamed him 'Humphrey' – the whale who had lost his way. However, at first that morning nobody could find Knucklehead. He could not have gone far, and so it was that reporters in a television news helicopter spotted him near the turning basin in the deep-water shipping channel just south of Sacramento, 92 miles from the ocean. Confused, Knucklehead was swimming in circles. He was in real danger of colliding with a ship or stranding on the outgoing tide. His skin was beginning to peel too, one of the effects of being in fresh water. The people onshore were becoming concerned for his health.

Along with the police and the coastguard, vets and biologists arrived. Heads were scratched, experts called, opinions sought, and a strategy drawn up. An underwater loudspeaker was lowered into the water from a boat on the seaward side of the young whale. Recordings of humpbacks were played, the idea being that Knucklehead would follow the sounds and the boat out to the sea, but he was having none of it. He ignored them all and continued his circling. There was more head scratching. The calls were modified and they had another go. Again Knucklehead paid little attention. A two-pronged attack was decided on.

The following day several boats went upriver of the whale and the people on board created a 'sound net'. They banged on metal tubes in the water, the unpleasant sound aimed at driving Knucklehead ahead of them. It was similar to a Japanese way of fishing known as *oikami*. At the same time, the boat playing the humpback feeding sounds led the way towards the sea; and it seemed to work. Two tugboats manoeuvred a cargo ship into dock, but when they were clear, Knucklehead swam slowly but surely down the Sacramento River, a flotilla of over 20 boats following not far behind him.

He passed through the pilings of a low, wooden bridge but at the Rio Vista Bridge he hesitated, and began to slap his tail on the water. Unsure whether he should pass under he began to circle again. A fireboat shot high-pressure jets of water to encourage Knucklehead to move again, but he would not budge. He appeared agitated so the boats backed off and waited, but Knucklehead just swam around and around. His skin had lost its shine and was dull and puckered up. Veterinarians watching from a boat voiced their concerns. A dart containing antibiotics was fired into his back, a precaution in case of infection. The rest of the day was quiet. The wind got up and the boats returned to their berths, but by now 10,000 people a day were coming to the riverside to gawp at him. Every time he surfaced a great cheer went up. It was an extraordinary event.

Another day and night passed, and the following morning Knucklehead had moved of his own accord. He had reached the saltier waters of Suisun Bay, about 45 miles from the ocean, but he stopped and circled again, reluctant to negotiate a trio of bridges at Benicia. His skin, however, already seemed to be better. Eventually, again without any encouragement, he headed down river. As he approached Carquinez Bridge, the chief cook at the local fish restaurant watching from the roof told diners that the whale was coming. Two hundred people, including bar staff, cooks and customers, crowded onto the pier and cheered as Knucklehead swam downstream. He made San Pablo Bay by late afternoon, and by nightfall he was circling again near Tiburon, only 10 miles from the Golden Gate Bridge. Under cover of darkness, Knucklehead made it to the open ocean. He was free once more, but left a little confused by his strange ordeal. He swam due west. As Knucklehead headed out, the body of a grey whale drifted in, victim of a ship collision. This whale would no longer be making the annual migration between the Bering Sea and Mexico's San Ignacio lagoon. It was another casualty in a crowded sea.

* * *

The sea tasted fresh after a sojourn in polluted river water. Knucklehead struck out towards the western horizon with renewed vigour. Something told him that this was the way to go. He was becoming more confident every minute, a remarkable transformation from a youngster who was totally dependent on his mother to a yearling with an iron will to survive. Little did he know, however, that he was moving boldly from the frying pan into the fire.

A huge frond of giant kelp, which had been torn from near-shore kelp forests, was a refuge for baby rockfish. There was also a queue of sunfish. These huge disc-shaped fish, up to six feet across, waited in an orderly line. At the front of the row, one lay still in the water with its open mouth pointing to the surface. It was a signal. The frond was a cleaning station and the sunfish were availing themselves of its services. Small fish darted out and gobbled up the parasites and dead skin, but there were some larger parasites that they could not budge. There were, however, others that could shift those irritations. Having been divested of the small fry, the sunfish drifted away from the cleaning station as another took its place. It then rose up to the surface, turned onto its side and waited. Sure enough, a few minutes later a gull dropped down, stood on the sunfish's floating body and began to stab at the most stubborn parasites.

Knucklehead, though, needed neither small fish nor gulls to clean him, and as he approached the Farallon Islands he was confronted by another hazard. It was a great white shark and it was big, a female almost 18 feet long. She was one of a small population of great whites that staked out the islands, patrolling a 'killing zone' just offshore. Here she intercepted seals and sea lions moving to and from the islands. The first elephant seals would be returning soon from feeding out in the open ocean, so the sharks were especially alert.

Knucklehead stopped. The shark circled, her round, black, soulless eyes looking intently at the young whale. He, in turn, used his long flippers to manoeuvre his body, just as he had seen his mother do, so that his powerful tail was ready to hit the shark should she attack. The two eyed each other. The shark was in no rush to make the first move. She played a waiting game. If the whale bolted she would seize the opportunity.

More usually, she would use surprise, approaching her victim from below and behind so it did not see her approach. Her attacks were intelligent too; she could tell the difference between seals and sea lions, two of her favourite prey. Seals propelled themselves with their powerful hind flippers, keeping their front flippers by their side. Sea lions swam with their front flippers, using their rear flippers as a rudder to steer. She would attack the hindquarters of a seal but bite into the midrib of a sea lion

– clever for a shark. In this way neither prey could escape. A young whale, though, was a different kind of prey altogether. The element of surprise had gone and the whale, though still a youngster, was 28 feet long with a powerful tail. The shark continued to circle menacingly but kept her distance. She looked for a weak point, an opportunity to dart in and take a quick bite. In Australia, great whites have been known to take chunks out of the flippers of humpbacks trapped in fishing nets. Knucklehead was ready to fight if he had to.

The shark saw her chance. Knucklehead had turned so that she was in his blind spot. She accelerated. Then, wham! A killer whale slammed into the shark. It rammed her at the shark's weakest point, the area of her gills. The shark was taken completely by surprise and was visibly hurt. The killer whale circled. It was a female with a companion. She rammed the shark again. They had caught and eaten a seal earlier in the morning but now they were having a go at this very large and dangerous shark. The larger orca rammed the shark repeatedly until it was dead and its innards were spilling into the sea. The smaller orca was towing the carcass through the water, when a large portion of liver popped out. She grabbed it and ate it.

Scientists working at the research station on Farallons watched the drama unfold. They knew the killer whales. The larger whale was CA2 and the smaller CA6, two members of the infamous L.A. Pod, known whale killers. It might well have been the pod that attacked Knucklehead and the other whales when he was separated from his mother. They often ran down grey whales and humpback whales on migration, killing their calves. This pod was dangerous, but only two of them were here. Knucklehead swam quickly and quietly away. The killers ignored him, continuing to nudge the shark carcass and feed on pieces of liver until it finally sank. There was, however, an unexpected outcome to the incident: all the great white sharks in the area suddenly disappeared. The returning elephant seals had an easy passage to the islands that winter. Usually they had to run a gauntlet of great white sharks.

Knucklehead dived to the seabed, passing the wreck of the *USS Independence*, a light aircraft carrier, which had survived intense wartime activity but was contaminated during the Bikini atom tests of 1946. It was later loaded with radioactive waste and sunk right here. Scattered across the sandy seabed were tens of thousands of steel barrels, each containing radioactive waste that was dumped in the ocean. Knucklehead surfaced, and in a series of shallow dives continued his journey.

Many seals were arriving from the southwest, so Knucklehead headed out in that direction, out over the edge of the continental shelf and into the open ocean. Several female seals passed him, but he ignored them. Instinct seemed to tell him to press on, but not long after he set out he was on a collision course with a gigantic fast-moving object in the sea. It was a blue whale. He slowed down as the giant slid past. It barely stopped to look, and it seemed to go on forever. It was 60 feet long, not huge for a blue whale but still pretty massive. These whales could be up to 100 feet long, the largest animals ever to have lived, but this whale seemed to be in a hurry. It was doing about 25 miles per hour, perhaps 30. The reason immediately became apparent – the killer whales at the Farallons had rejoined with their pod and they were pursuing the larger whale – it was the infamous L.A. Pod and some close relatives.

The attackers were smaller than most other killer whales and their communication sounds were like no other pod, but they showed a similar division of labour as the orcas that attacked Knucklehead and his mother. Several killers flanked the blue whale on either side. Two others swam ahead to try to slow it down, and two trailed behind to stop any escape. One group pushed down on the whale's head, attempting to stop it from breathing, and another swam underneath, preventing it from diving. The blue's tail flukes were shredded, like the old humpback's had been, but it was still able to swim. A large bull orca led in forays to bite off chunks of flesh. The whale, however, kept swimming and despite being harassed continually by the killers, it continued to do so for a further five agonising hours, by which time the large pod broke off and looked for easier prey…and they found it, a grey whale and her yearling offspring.

The killers regrouped and followed the two larger whales at a discreet distance. They swam slowly and silently, taking time to recover from their earlier attack. When the time was right and at a signal from the matriarch, the pod took off. They caught up with the grey whales in no time, and began the long and arduous task of wearing them down. It took another six hours before the two whales were brought to a halt. The mother turned belly up and the youngster swam above her, but it was no good. Like living torpedoes, the killers rammed them incessantly, and bit at their flukes and fins. One killer was tasked with wedging herself between the two whales. She pushed and then rammed the smaller whale in its soft underbelly, causing it to deviate from its course. It was the moment she was waiting for. She eased herself between them, separating the youngster from its mother. Others swam over the top and prevented the young whale from surfacing. While two larger orcas tore at its lower jaw for the prized 500-pound tongue, the others ripped off large chunks of blubber. The head separated from the body, and the remains sank down eventually to the seabed.

The first to pick up the smell were hagfish. They followed the odour to its source and hit a food bonanza. A whale fall, even a whale mangled by killer whales, was a rarity on the sea floor. Using their circular mouths, they burrowed into the flesh and blubber, eating the corpse from the inside out. They did not have the feast to themselves for long. All manner of deep-sea creatures began to arrive. Squat lobsters, crabs, brittlestars and starfish crawled across the bottom sediments and clambered onto the body. Rattail fish, a small octopus and a swarm of thousands of shrimp-like amphipods, each with jaws that are as sharp as a surgeon's scalpel, joined the throng, and there were more to come. The larvae of bone-eating zombie worms, tube-worms, centipede-like polychaete worms, clams, mussels and the medusa stages of tiny, white sea anemones, all of which had been drifting in the water column, settled amongst the scavengers, ready to grow into adults that would thrive on the leftovers, including the bones. Already bacteria began to settle and grow. These bacteria converted any oily tissue into sulphides that would sustain animals normally found close to deep-sea hydrothermal vents. They would use the carcass as a 'stepping stone' to the next underwater hot spring. But for now, it was the mobile scavengers that held sway, and one of the largest swam languidly in to take its rightful place at table.

It was a Pacific sleeper shark, and it was doing what sleeper sharks were generally thought to do – it was scavenging. It was also a monster, 23 feet long, putting it among the largest sharks on the planet. It moved in a kind of permanent slow motion, its large spade-like tail only capable of short bursts of speed. Its enlarged olfactory bulbs had detected no more than a few molecules of dead whale from over a mile away, and its scoop-like jaws were ready to strip off any fat-rich blubber that the killer whales had left. Surrounded by writhing hagfish, it worked the corpse systematically, pausing to tear away protein-rich muscle here and chunks of blubber there.

Up at the surface, a female elephant seal startled Knucklehead. She popped up right beside him. She took a few breaths and three minutes later dived back down again, disappearing into the deep. She was fishing for squid about 2,500 feet down. She slept on the way down and on the way up, so saving energy. For Knucklehead, though, the prospect of finding food here was low. It was time to fast. He probably would not feed again until his return to Alaska the following summer. He had fed well on his mother's milk and he had picked up additional calories off the coast of Oregon, so he had sufficient blubber to carry him through.

*   *   *

For several days, Knucklehead continued on the same southwesterly course across the wide Pacific Ocean. It led him to more southerly latitudes. The water was becoming noticeably warmer, and the traffic heavier. A school of bluefin tuna flashed past. They were on one of their trans-Pacific crossings from spawning sites off Japan to feeding sites in the eastern Pacific. Their bodies were maintained at a temperature warmer than the surrounding seawater, enabling them to work faster and more efficiently. They swam with their mouths open, for they had to force water over their gills to ensure sufficient oxygen reached their turbocharged muscles. To help them find their way they had magnetite particles, not in the brain like hump-backs but in neural pits in their snout. These were thought to enable them to navigate using the Earth's geomagnetic field. Passing at a more leisurely pace was a loggerhead sea turtle. Knucklehead was once more in the trans-Pacific highway. If he followed the corridor, he would find Hawaii, the place of his birth – and maybe his mother. He swam on.

He came to a large oilcan floating at the surface. A triggerfish had made it his territory and defended it against all-comers, darting out aggressively should any other fish approach too close. All around, small fish had adopted other flotsam as temporary homes. It was the only cover available in the open ocean. A wahoo, a large, dark-blue predatory fish, trailed a raft of flotsam, ready to grab any baitfish that came to hide beneath it. A thick line of plankton marked the boundary between two ocean currents, and a huge crowd of small fishes were feasting on it. All of a sudden, the scattered crowd became a huge, tightly packed ball. The fish had detected vibrations in the water and they were frightened. There were bigger fish coming. The smaller fish whirled around in a huge black carousel, the ball changing shape like a single writhing animal.

A party of jacks arrived, but they were cautious about entering this dense seething mass. They darted this way and that looking for an entry. But then a school of bonitos appeared, and they did not hesitate. They launched the first attacks. The smaller fish panicked and broke into fragmented bait balls. It was the chance the jacks had been waiting for and they too tore into the helpless fish. Then, to cap it all, yellowfin tuna moved in, picking off their victims one by one. Fish leapt from the surface to escape their pursuers, but the shearwaters were there and ready. They swooped in from above to claim their share of the spoils. Eventually, all that was left was a dead fish floating upside down at the surface. A yellowfin shot up, grabbed it and the entire fish ball was gone.

* * *

By the evening of that same day, Knucklehead was resting at the surface when he became aware that he was very far from alone. He was lolling about in a surprisingly crowded ocean. He was surrounded by a dense swarm of tiny, transparent, barrel-shaped tubes, each about the size of a thumb. They were salps, and each little tube was an eating factory. It sucked water and plankton in at one end, filtered out the food particles with a minuscule slime net, and ejected water and waste from out of the other end. These tiny barrels were jet propelled. Moving and eating were the same to a salp – a jelly ramjet, and its feeding system was almost industrial. The mucus net resembled a conveyor belt, produced at one end of the barrel and then devoured at the other along with any food particles that stuck to it. There were also passengers – amphipods, similar to those on the jellyfish. They nibbled away at the salp's insides, but for some reason they seemed to be tolerated. As long as they did not damage a vital organ or sever a blood vessel, most of those salps lived a normal life despite their unhelpful stowaways. Some, though, were nothing more than hollow tubes. Their insides had been eaten by pregnant female amphipods, which deposited their eggs inside. A few had tiny crabs riding inside the tube, and still others harboured tiny fish. They were tiny islands in the open sea.

The great swarm of salps had come up from a thousand feet below to feed at the surface during the night, and it was so big it covered tens of thousands of square miles of the sea's surface. Some had formed into chains, making hollow, snakelike tubes, many several feet in length and a few up to 50 feet long.

Hundreds of harmless moon jellyfish, some with juvenile jacks hiding below their bell, and the occasional lion's mane jellyfish, with its thick clusters of stinging tentacles, drifted in the current too. A purple jellyfish glowed in the dark. And, as Knucklehead swam though the water, every time he propelled himself forwards the sea around him sparkled with bioluminescent algae. It was an extraordinary sight – a long, luminous wake trailing behind a glowing whale.

By morning the salps had returned to the deep sea, but there was a steady stream of young turtles heading towards the east while Knucklehead was heading west. He was about half way between the American mainland and Hawaii when there in

117

front of him was a great white shark. A little further on he met another, and another. The place was overrun with them. A large male swam almost leisurely towards the young whale, its dark, triangular dorsal fin and the tip of its tail cutting through the sea's surface. Sensing the whale ahead, it turned and circled slowly. A smaller shark, finding itself in the same patch of sea, hurried away. Size was everything in the shark's world. The larger shark, though, seemed uninterested in Knucklehead. After a few minutes at the surface, both sharks dived and swam into the depths, down to a thousand feet or more. They remained there for 10 minutes or so, and then swam back to the surface. They repeated the manoeuvre over and over again. This was 'White Shark Café', a mysterious meeting place for great white sharks in the northern Pacific. Most of them had travelled all the way from California to be here, but why they went to this place and what they were doing here was, and still is, unknown.

CHAPTER SEVEN
HAWAII HOME

Knucklehead reached Hawaii several weeks after the other whales. Many took little more than a month to make the journey from Alaska to Maui, but he had been delayed by his unexpected and eventful detour. A few of the 6,000 humpbacks that come here each northern winter had already calved or mated, but as he approached the island of Maui it was not new life that greeted him but death. A large sperm whale had washed up on the shore. It had already been towed 35 miles out to sea in the hope that it would sink in deep waters, but it had drifted in again. The carcass was in the shallows, and an oil slick stretched for several miles down current. Several tiger sharks had followed the odour trail, and the water was deep enough for them to venture close to take a bite.

They lined up and took their turn, one shark feeding at a time. It carefully aligned itself with the carcass and with a few thrusts of its tail it slammed into the side of the whale, its square snout rising up from the water as it took out a great crescent-shaped bite of blubber and skin. It shook its head violently from side to side so its razor-sharp, saw-like teeth hacked through the flesh. One shark turned on its side for better leverage, taking a 10- or 20-pound chunk of the energy-rich blubber. They fed for five minutes, and squabbled for 10, the latter determining who was next in line. The largest sharks jumped the queue. Size was on their side.

The usual cloud of gulls and other seabirds crowded around, looking for scraps. Some tried to stand on top of the whale, but the skin was so slippery they continually slipped off, almost into the jaws of the sharks below. But as the carcass began to drift out on the tide, another shark appeared, not a tiger or one of the more familiar Hawaiian sharks but a great white. It was here, in the middle of the Pacific Ocean, thousands of miles from known white shark habitats. It was 'Tipfin', a young male known to shark scientists. He was part of the great white shark exodus at the time of the killer whale attack near the Farallon Islands. To avoid becoming a victim himself, he had dived down to 1,500 feet and hightailed it out of there...all the way to Hawaii.

Knucklehead gave the dead whale and its attendants a wide berth, but no sooner was he out of range than the sperm whale exploded. Gases from decomposition had built up inside the whale's body and suddenly it had ripped apart. Blubber, oil and pieces of skin flew everywhere, killing several seabirds and covering spectators on the beach with blood and entrails. A large chunk of blubber landed on a car and crushed its canvas roof. The rest fell into the sea, triggering a feeding frenzy of astronomical proportions. Every living thing in the area rushed in to grab a morsel – big fish, small fish, gulls and sharks. Knucklehead sped away from the mayhem, and by evening the bickering had ceased.

The tiger sharks did not patrol the same piece of shoreline all year round as was once thought – they were not defending territories; instead, they wandered through the archipelago, pitching up at places where food was seasonally plentiful.

The previous summer, during June and July, many of them patrolled islands in the northwest – the French Frigate Shoals, where fledgling albatrosses were learning how to fly. The birds flapped vigorously while standing on the beach and when the trade winds blew up at midday, they were lifted into the air and they flew momentarily, sometimes disastrously. A few ditched in the sea, and the tiger sharks were waiting. They had arrived several days before the birds were ready to take off. How they knew when to be there was a mystery, but they arrived like clockwork at exactly the same time as in previous years.

At first the sharks were unsuccessful. They approached the birds from below but their bow waves pushed them away. Later in the season, they either wised up or somehow remembered the best technique. They rushed across the surface, grabbed birds and dragged them below, where they drowned. Now, however, there were no chicks trying to get airborne, so the sharks were looking elsewhere.

In fact, by the time Knucklehead had reached the islands at the eastern end of the Hawaiian chain, the adult albatrosses at the western end were returning from a spell feeding at sea. The males had arrived first, the females a week later, and they were taking up where they left off with their lifelong partners. Each female would be laying a single egg and, in the predator-free environment of a remote island such as Tern Island, the pair would be devoting the next few months to first incubating the eggs for a couple of months and then rearing the chick for a further six, and maybe more. Both the female and her partner would be taking it in turns to travel extraordinary distances to find food for their offspring. During a four-month period, one female was tracked for nearly 39,000 miles.

Her wings were long and narrow, stiff and cambered with a thickened and streamlined leading edge to give a superb aerofoil cross-section. When in the air, tendons provided a shoulder lock, so her wings were extended without her having to use her muscles. In order to keep aloft she rarely flapped; instead, she used 'dynamic soaring'. She dived into the still air in the troughs between waves with the wind behind her. In this way she gathered speed. Then she turned and swooped back into the air, where she was exposed to a headwind that took her high enough for another 'wheeling' manoeuvre. She also used 'slope soaring', in which she maintained altitude by riding the wind blowing up the face of a wave. She travelled about 66 feet horizontally for every three feet dropped vertically, a glide ratio of 22:1, and using these patterns of flying she could over great distances for minimum energy consumption. It was so efficient, her heart rate when flying was not far off the rate when she sat on her nest. With such a dependence on the wind and waves, however, meant that on calm, wind-free days the bird had to put down and wait on the sea's surface for the wind to pick up again. Take off and landing also tended to be a hit-and-miss affair, and dependent very much on wind speed.

Her food was mainly squid and fish taken at the surface, for she dived no deeper than three or four feet. When she returned to the nest – a straight-line, non-stop journey that was more than a thousand miles – she regurgitated first partly digested squid and fish, and when that ran out she produced an oily substance, the result of digesting the first creatures that she caught. She had reared many a strapping young bird that might live 50 years or more, but other less fortunate parents were providing the annual feast for tiger sharks.

* * *

Knucklehead's day started quietly. Clouds obscured the sun, and a brisk northeasterly breeze put a chop on the sea. Whale-watching boats were already out on the sea and the first tourists of the day were already admiring Knucklehead. The boat circled him two or three times before moving on in search of more flamboyant whales. Knucklehead breached, swam a bit, and breached again, but there was no reply.

In the centre of the island, the last Hawaiian petrel fledglings were leaving from their nest burrows on the rim of the Haleakala Crater. After calling for their parents one last time in an untidy chorus of yaps, barks and squeals, they left their burrows and took to the air. Most had gone in the night, leaving a few stragglers to go to sea, at first light. Some flew north and others west. They were the lucky ones. Feral cats and introduced mongooses killed many of the season's chicks. The survivors headed out to sea where they would be feeding at the surface on squid, lanternfish and goatfish. They flew erratically in a characteristically high arching and swooping flight. They were once prized birds, only eaten by Hawaiian royalty; today, they are protected.

Knucklehead swam along the southern shoreline of Maui, the steep slopes of the dormant volcano to his north, and Kanaloa Point – named after one of the four primary Hawaiian gods – coming up on his right. Along the shore are the remains of ancient fishing villages and naturally occurring achialine ponds – depressions in the solidified lava fed by freshwater springs. The level of the brackish pond water rises and falls with the tide, and even here the daily struggle of life and death was in evidence. The ponds were lined with golden-orange algal mats and colonised by small red shrimps – the ÿpae'ula – that wriggled through lava tubes and cracks in the rocks. Using their tiny pincers, they grazed on the algae and bacteria. They would live to a ripe old age – up to 20 years old, if the larger red predatory shrimps did not get them first. The ancient Hawaiians once used the ponds as fish farms, a tradition that continues to this day.

Rounding the southwest tip of Maui and passing Keone'o'io or La Pereuse Bay, Knucklehead heard the unmistakeable sounds of dolphins. They were spinner dolphins; the very same school with which the young whale had played all those months ago. Keone'o'io was their base and daytime resting place. They were swimming quietly up and down when Knucklehead passed by, but as soon as they spotted him, they crowded around. It was fun time all over again. They corkscrewed and swooped, rode on the whale's bow wave and curled around his back, clicking, buzzing and whirring continuously. One dolphin leapt clear of the water and spun almost 360 degrees in mid-air before plunging back below. Others followed, until the entire school was leaping and spinning.

Knucklehead was reluctant to leave but instinct told him he should press on to the place where he was born. He headed towards Molokini, the rim of an extinct volcanic crater. Half of it was above water, forming a crescent moon-shaped island, and half was below, creating a sheltered reef. There were many dive boats anchored over the crater, with many anchor lines. Knucklehead kept well clear. Great swathes of damaged coral were evidence of dragging anchors.

A school of grey reef sharks patrolled the outer slopes of the cone and a handful of white-tip reef sharks lay under the lava ledges of 'Shark Condo'. Visibility here was remarkable, up to 150 feet, the clearest water in Hawaii. A flight of eagle rays swooped by, their extraordinarily long, thin tails trailing behind them. As their shadows crossed the sea floor, a spiny lobster raced for cover, but these rays were more interested in clams, oysters and sea urchins, and the occasional shrimp or octopus. An enormous shoal of convict tang, their striped body pattern resembling a convict's clothes, suddenly scattered like an explosion as a larger fish threatened. They regrouped and drove off a bunch of damselfish that had been fiercely guarding a patch of the algae that both species are fond of and feed on. A trumpetfish, resembling more a stick than a fish, was well camouflaged amongst the seaweeds, but it broke cover and shadowed a shy peacock grouper, dashing out occasionally to steal its meal.

A pair of Moorish idols, partners for life, searched for sponges, and black triggerfish flapped across flat patches of sand. A large catamaran cruised overhead, carrying a party of snorkelling enthusiasts to the submerged crater. Another group of spinner dolphins kept them company. A monk seal, the world's rarest seal, eased itself away from the increasingly crowded reef and set out for the Back Wall, which dropped down vertically for 350 feet.

There were no whales around, so Knucklehead pressed on towards the Au'au Channel, where they were usually to be found. None were to be seen at first, but gradually he became aware of distant singing. The lowest notes, like blasts from an overenthusiastic foghorn, were audible at first, but as he approached closer to the singer the higher, piccolo-type chirping sounds could be heard too. The singer was massive, a mature bull at least 50 feet long. He lay in the water column at a depth of 50 feet, his head pointing downwards, his body at an angle of about 45° and his tail appearing to hang on an invisible hook. The lowest notes penetrated Knucklehead's entire body, while the upper registers were ear-splitting. Knucklehead watched and listened as if in a trance. Scientists studying the whales referred to him as a 'joiner'. It was as if he were learning the song – the maestro and the pupil.

The songs themselves were like bird song, only they went on for 15 or 20 minutes, and they were surprisingly complex. They had their own syntax, each song broken down into repeated phrases that, in turn, were made up of individual sound units. Each sound unit varied in frequency across a sound spectrum similar to that audible to the human ear. Some sounds were frequency modulated – that is, the pitch went up or down; others remained at the same frequency; and still others were amplitude modulated, meaning they went louder and quieter. The phrases were built of short segments of about six units, while longer segments had up to 400 units. Several repeated phrases constituted a theme, and several themes made up a song.

The songs were not akin to human language, but elements of language could be heard in the hierarchical nature of the songs. And all the bulls in Hawaiian waters were singing the same song. The moans, cries and chirps followed a particular pattern that was gradually evolving during the course of the mating season, sometimes rapidly, other times more slowly. A frequency sweep would be flattened here and a sound unit might get louder there.

What is more, the whales in Mexico and Japan were singing a similar song, with only slight variations, and humpbacks in the Atlantic and Indian oceans, and in the southern Pacific were all singing their own ocean-wide songs, quite different to the songs sung by whales in the northern Pacific.

The speed that those sounds travelled through water was four times faster than sounds travel through air. For this reason, sound was a natural medium of communication for Knucklehead. His other senses were limited. Smell was slow and vision restricted. The young whale, like most whales and dolphins, was using sound.

The older males sang mainly, but not exclusively, on the winter breeding grounds so the songs must have had something to do with flirting with females or spacing out males, or were even a sound competition between bulls. Whatever the reason for the large bull to sing, Knucklehead was receiving the full blast. He stayed watching and listening as another large bull arrived and circled the singer. No females showed any interest, but the two bulls continued the stand-off until they swam away together towards another group of males; then the large group unexpectedly sped off.

The largest whale in the group had spotted a female and her escort about a mile away. How he knew she was there was another mystery, for he could not have seen her. Maybe he picked up the low-pitched notes from the intimate calls she was exchanging with her escort or maybe he had seen her blow on the horizon. Whichever way, he was now powering through the water at 15 miles per hour with a gang of mainly smaller males, many of them juveniles, in tow. Knucklehead followed at a discreet distance, and had to put on a burst of speed to keep up.

The group of rowdy males swam directly towards the female, trying to separate her from her escort. He swung around his huge body, placing his bulk between the boisterous group and his temporary partner, and then the two made off, the female in the lead and the other males in pursuit. The escort let out a long stream of bubbles, much like a destroyer producing a smokescreen, hiding the female from view as they tried to make their escape; but the young males were not going to give up that easily. They ploughed on, bursting through the bubble cloud. They began to push and shove, trying desperately to displace the large male from his position next to the female.

The largest intruder, the bull Knucklehead had been watching as he sang, slammed into the main escort, pushing him momentarily off course. It was just enough for one of the young bulls to usurp his position. Another large bull pushed the young pretender out of the way, ramming him almost broadside. The youngster, bloodied but undeterred, dropped back and Knucklehead almost ran into him. Up ahead, the fight was only just beginning.

The usurped male tried to regain his position. He slewed sideways into the new escort but failed to dislodge him. The new escort, in turn, swelled his throat to appear larger, while the smaller whales behind blocked out any chance that he could sneak in behind. As the new escort rose to breathe, the former escort rose up onto his head and pushed it under. He was barely able to take a breath when the full weight of the other whale came down on him. He turned sideways and began to strike his adversary with his long flippers. The other whale slammed him with his tail, and then was jostled away again by the younger whales. They seemed to be working together, a bachelor party backing up the two larger contenders. The second male did not attack his associate, but seemed to be there to give some sort of support, blocking out the former escort, ensuring he could not get back into the race. The rowdy youngsters continued to harass him; they crowded around him but he struck back, butting the smaller whales with his barnacle-encrusted snout.

The water began to redden with blood. The smaller whales were taking a pasting. They were learning how to fight the hard way. Knucklehead trailed behind the group, while more whales joined in. There were now upwards of 12 whales in the mêlée. With them came another large bull, which began to attack the two larger whales, trying to displace the new escort. He was a formidable fighter, the champion of many skirmishes. He used superior strength to ease aside the second whale, bringing him right next to the new escort. He rose up on the other whale's back, preventing him from reaching the surface, and then crashed his snout into his head. Like an underwater gymnast, he twisted this way and that, each move preventing his opponent from surfacing. He would have to breathe soon, and so the escort broke away, leaving the way open to the new arrival. He took station next to the female, but it was not over yet.

The two pals swam back through the flotilla of younger males and came up on either side of the large bull. They slammed into him on both flanks, turning their bodies so they could use their powerful tails to rain down blow and after blow. It was a gargantuan battle, during which more blood flowed. Pieces of skin and blubber were left floating in the water, food for the ubiquitous gulls that accompanied the skirmish.

The three contestants bellowed and moaned, and each time they surfaced the exchange of air through their blowholes sounded like an express train. Their backs arched through the ocean's surface and they dived below, the water churned into a pink froth. One bull raised its body right out of the water, and then dropped backed down – a 'reversal', which made him seem bigger than he really was. He breached, smashed his chin on the surface, and tail slapped, showing off to the other males. It was his first mistake. The other large bulls turned on him, again slamming into him from either side. This was one fight he would not win. While they thrashed around, the original escort was able to slip in and take up his former position next to the female. He had won the day. The other males peeled off eventually and swam away

The female meanwhile seemed oblivious to the turmoil behind and beside her, or at least she feigned ignorance. In reality, it was she who was calling the shots. She would select her partner on the basis of his prowess in battle. She continued along the surface in a series of shallow dives. She had set the pace, not the jostling males, but with the others gone Knucklehead could see whom the bulls had been fighting over. It was his mother.

He hesitated, and then surged ahead to try to catch up with her. The primary escort mistaking him for another suitor made a big sweep with one of his flippers, blocking him out and forcing him to stop. The two adult whales pushed on, leaving Knucklehead behind. A pair of bottlenose dolphins suddenly appeared and began to nip at the tail flukes of the large escort. They swam around him, and he tried to shrug them off like bothersome flies. The group swam off into the blue.

Knucklehead waited. Maybe they would return. He called but there was no answer. For a second time, he felt very alone. His mother was gone, he sensed this time for good. Now, he had to put to good use all that he had learned during the first year in his life...all the lessons and experiences, even the fateful period of early separation. He was already learning the way of whales.

A loud moan, though, revealed he was not alone after all. There was another whale right there beside him, another yearling who had just been abandoned by its mother. As the blurred shape materialised into an identifiable whale, Knucklehead could see it was the young female with the white flippers. She circled him, calmly and inquisitively. He responded, moving gently around. It was a form of play, not the play of calves, but of young adults. It was a courtship ballet, not the real thing, but a dress rehearsal. It would be several years before either whale would be ready to take a partner and mate, but this was a beginning.

POSTSCRIPT

Knucklehead grew up to be fine humpback bull. He bore the killer whale tooth marks on his tail flukes for the rest of his life, and a few more besides. He made the journey between Hawaii and southeast Alaska many times, and took in California and Mexico too. He had countless face-offs with killer whales, but always came away without serious injury. He tagged along with competitive groups when he was about five years old, and he was often seen as a joiner, listening and learning the traditional humpback songs, but he was not a successful suitor for a long while. He started to sing in earnest when he was 10, and then things began to happen. He became a successful primary escort, and he attracted his first mate. No one knows whether his first partner was the white-flippered female, but she was certainly in the area at about the right time. Since then, he has sired a good few calves.

Knucklehead's alter ego, the loveable Humphrey, was actually named by a *San Francisco Chronicle* newspaper reporter who attributed the christening to a local restaurant owner. While known as Humphrey, he had several books written about him, and he was the star of many television films. He appeared on countless T-shirts, and there was even a 'Humphrey the Humpback Bus', carrying an almost life-size hand-painted picture of Humphrey by environmental artist George Sumner on its side. A granite memorial commemorating his visit to Rio Vista stands beside the Sacramento River. The local pizza house named a pizza after him, and plastic whale toys were re-branded 'Humphrey' in order for them to sell.

In 1990, while on one of his many migrations between Alaska, Hawaii and Mexico, he pitched up in San Francisco Bay again. On this second occasion, he stranded on a mud bank to the north of Sierra Point near Candlestick Park and had to be pulled off in a cargo net by the US Coast Guard. In 1991, there were unconfirmed sightings of the whale off the Farallon Islands, to the west of San Francisco. This was the last that was heard of Knucklehead.

NOTES ON HUMPBACK
WHALES

Evolution

Strange as it may seem, the ancestry of humpback whales can
be traced back to animals that lived on land, probably even-
toed ungulates or artiodactyls, a group today that includes
hippos, pigs, cattle, deer and camels. The whale's earliest
ancestors, however, did not live in the sea but probably beside
streams. Some were wolf-size; others coyote-size; and members
of one species resembled otters, only they had exceptionally
long snouts. Some moved to the coastal swamps and eventually
into inshore waters of what was then the warm and shallow
Tethys Sea.

These first whale ancestors probably waded into the water to
feed. Their legs shortened, their bodies and jaws became more
elongated and they developed powerful tails. Gradually they
became more amphibious in their lifestyle, feeding in shallow
coastal waters, estuaries and rivers, but coming out onto land to
rest and reproduce, much like seals and sea lions do today.

Eventually, 35–40 million years ago, these archaeocetes, as
they are known, took on a more fish-like, torpedo shape, and a
dorsal fin on the back helped in hydrodynamic control. It

133

stopped them slewing from side to side when they swam. They gave up the flexible neck and the coat disappeared, relying on blubber to keep warm. Front limbs developed into flippers and the hind limbs were much reduced to the point that there was no need for a pelvic girdle.

The 60ft (18m) long *Basilosaurus*, for example, had a small pair of vestigial hind limbs projecting from its body, but these were not connected to the animal's main skeletal frame. Nostrils migrated from the front of the face to the top of the head, and ways were developed to seal them from water. The ear bones were quite distinct from those in other mammals, in that the jawbone conducted sounds to the ear, from which signals were sent via nerves to the brain. Sight and smell were less important, so the brain specialised in the processing of sound information. These animals spent most, if not all, of their time in the sea.

About 25 million years ago, two main types of recognisable whales evolved: the odontocetes, or toothed whales, which had teeth and developed a sophisticated echolocation system for finding their way about and searching for food; and the mysticetes, or baleen whales, which had baleen instead of teeth for straining food from seawater and which grew to enormous size. The blue whale, at up to 108ft (33m) long and weighing up to 190 tonnes, is not only the largest living whale, but also the largest creature ever to have lived on the Earth.

The archaeocetes had teeth differentiated into canines, incisors and molars, but by the time the odontocetes evolved, all the teeth were sharp and peg-like. The mysticetes, on the other hand, developed their specialised baleen plates that evolved from curved transverse ridges in the palate. During the early stages of foetal development, modern baleen whales have tooth buds, an indication that both types of modern whales probably developed from a common ancestor.

Whales and dolphins, while taking on the general shape of

fish in order to move effectively through the relatively dense medium of water, have a horizontal tale that moves vertically, rather than a vertical tail that moves in a horizontal plane like the tail of sharks and ichthyosaurs. It is thought that this developed because of the whale's constant need to surface to breathe. A downward thrust of the tail serves to lift the head to the surface so the blowhole can break surface more easily.

The earliest baleen whale fossils found so far are from the skeleton of *Aetiocetus*. It was excavated in Oregon, and dated late Oligocene. Its skull and jaws show features shared with baleen whales, but it had a full set of teeth. However, by the Miocene epoch, 23.8–5.3 million years ago, whales from both major groups swam the seas, and all the major cetacean groups were evolving. They were smaller than today's giants, but what they lacked in size, they more than made up for in numbers.

With such a glut of species, inevitably something came along to take advantage of it; and that something was *Megalodon* – *Carcharodon* (*Carcharocles*) *meagalodon* – meaning 'big tooth', the largest and most powerful predatory shark ever to have lived, and an ancient relative of the modern great white shark. It was the largest of a group of lamniform sharks that evolved alongside the whales and dolphins, and preyed on them. It was up to 60ft (18m) long – a giant compared to the great white, which is 33ft (10m) long at most. It would have had to eat at least 2,000lb (900kg) of food a day, and there were plenty of whales around at the time to match its appetite. Fossil whale vertebrae and other bones have been found with the telltale scratch marks of a *megalodon* bite, so with a monster like this roaming the seas, it is a wonder any whales evolved at all; but they did.

Megalodon died out about 1.5 million years ago, due probably to climate change and a reduction in the number of whale species and therefore the number of whales available as food. The world became cooler and Ice Ages overwhelmed the higher latitudes. Whales developed blubber to keep themselves warm. They fed in food-rich cool temperate and cold polar seas, but returned to the tropics to drop their calves. It gave rise to the exceptionally long migrations that we see today.

The earliest humpback species to be excavated was *Megaptera miocaena* from rocks of the Upper Miocene in California, but the earliest fossils of a modern humpback whale, *Megaptera novaeangliae*, were discovered in a quarry by students from the Kogane Senior High School, Japan. The rocks are estimated to be 125,000–150,000 years old.

Vital statistics

Humpback whales are among the world's largest animals, not as long or as heavy as a blue whale, but still pretty hefty. Fully mature males grow to over 50ft (15m) long, while females can be slightly longer and larger, up to 56ft (17m) long and weigh over 36 tonnes. The largest humpback whale reliably measured was 62ft (19m) long and had flippers 20ft (6m) long, but the largest ever was supposedly a female killed off Bermuda that was claimed to have been 88ft (27m) long.

The humpback tail flukes can be 15ft (5m) across, and are deeply notched at the centre and serrated along the trailing edge. The pectoral fins are 15ft (5m) long on average. The dorsal fin is no more than 12in (30cm) high.

The head is proportionately large compared to the rest of the body. There are rows of protuberances, known as tubercles, along the head and lower jaw, each with a single hair. Under the chin is a large, irregular-shaped bump that enlarges with age and which is often covered with barnacles. The upper jaw is narrower than the lower jaw. Long pleats run from the chin to the navel. The eye is dark brown with a kidney-shaped pupil, and the ear opening is just 0.24in (6mm) wide and located behind and below the eye.

136

Humpbacks have the greatest thickness of blubber for the size of whale, and second in absolute thickness to blue whales. It varies at different times of the year, thicker at the end of summer, after a spell on the feeding grounds, than at the beginning of spring, when they are leaving their winter breeding sites.

Males and females are difficult to tell apart, except by the trained eye. On the underside, the female can be distinguished from the male by a distinct hemispherical lobe in the position of the genital slit. The male's penis is retained inside a genital slit so for most of the year it is not visible.

After a gestation period of 11–12 months, a pregnant female gives birth to a single calf. It is enormous, up to 15ft (5m) long and weighing 1.4 tonnes.

The maximum age of a humpback whale is unknown, but a female whale in the Gulf of Maine sub-population is known to be at least 38 years old, with no signs of old age. And, in the Glacier Bay–Icy Strait area of Alaska, a male humpback, known as Garfunkle, which has been tracked since his first year, reached 34 years old in 2008. Longevity estimates vary from 40 to 60 years, but as bowheads and right whales are thought to live to be 200, there may be some surprises to come.

What's in a name?

The humpback whale's pectoral fins or flippers are the longest of any whale, and they gave rise to the humpback's scientific name *Megaptera novaeangliae*, meaning 'big-winged New Englander'. The coastal waters of New England are historic feeding grounds, where French zoologist Mathurin Jacques Brisson (1723–1806) first described the whale as 'baleine de la Nouvelle Angleterre' in his *Regnum Animale* (1756). German zoologist Georg Heinrich Borowski provided its first scientific name in 1781. A year previously, it had already been named

Balaena boops, meaning the 'ox-eyed whale', by Danish missionary and naturalist Otto Fabricius (1744–1822) in his *Fauna Groenlandica* (1780), but the name had already been assigned to the fin whale, so Borowski gave it the scientific name *Balaena novaeangliae*.

In 1846, English zoologist John Edward Gray (1800–1875) proposed that the humpback should be in a separate genus to the other baleen whales (*Balaenoptera* spp.). He gave it the genus name *Megaptera*. The species name, however, was another problem. Each time a new stock was discovered in a different part of the world, it was given a separate species name. At one stage, there were 23 different species. It was realised eventually that all belonged to the same species and the scientific name *Megaptera novaeangliae* was adopted for them all, a name which persists to this day.

Big-winged New Englander

The extraordinarily long pectoral fins or flippers afford humpbacks considerable manoeuvrability, but they could well have other functions. The large surface area of the flippers might also help in temperature control, especially as whales travel between warm subtropical and cool temperate and polar waters. Along their leading edge are more tubercles, giving the fin a serrated look. They help make the fin hydro-dynamically efficient.

In laboratory tests, during which scientists placed flipper shapes in wind tunnels, they discovered that a flipper with tubercles had 32 per cent less drag and 8 per cent improvement in lift compared to the smooth-edged flipper found on other species of whales. The tubercles channel the water into separate water streams that accelerate across the surface of the flipper into organised, rotating flows. It is these vortices that help generate lift. It also means the angle of attack (or 'stall' angle in aeronautical terms) of the flipper can be 40 per cent steeper. This helps during feeding or repelling attackers. If one flipper is angled to increase lift, and the other to decrease lift, it gives the animal the ability to roll or make tight turns. The same angle from both flipper gives the whale the ability to make steep climbs or descents. Engineers are now copying the humpback flipper to make more efficient blades for wind turbines. Others are looking at similar applications in the design of aircraft wings, submarine hydroplanes and ships' rudders.

Distribution

Humpback whales are found in all the world's major oceans and seas. In most regions it is a migratory species, travelling between cool water, high latitude feeding grounds and subtropical or tropical breeding sites in both the northern and southern hemispheres.

North Pacific

In the North Pacific, whales mainly spend the winter around Hawaii, Japan, Mexico or Taiwan, and the summer in waters off Alaska, the Aleutian Islands, Kamchatka and the Sea of Okhotsk. A study of the North Pacific humpback population published in 2008 under the SPLASH initiative reports that 18,000–20,000 humpbacks currently reside in this part of the Pacific, having recovered from an estimated 1,500 whales directly after the commercial whaling ban was introduced in 1986. Some whales have even been seen in the Beaufort Sea, to the north of Alaska and Canada, the consequence possibly of global warming and the opening of the Northwest Passage.

North Atlantic

The northwest Atlantic population breeds in the balmy waters of the Caribbean, in shallow bank areas, such as Silver Bank,

Nividad Bank and the Bay of Samaná, off the Dominican Republic. They also over-winter off Puerto Rico, the Bahamas and Venezuela, births peaking in January and February. They journey the length of North America's east coast as far north as Greenland, Iceland and even across the Atlantic to Norway for the summer.

On the east coast of the USA, the Gulf of Maine is favoured by one sub-population of whales. They feed as far north as Nova Scotia and as far south as New York, as well as offshore over Stellwagen Bank and Georges Bank. They feast on sand eels, small herring and mackerel, and occasionally krill. Youngsters tend to be weaned before the journey south in the autumn, and many juveniles do not make the full migration back to the Caribbean but feed in the warm but productive waters of the Gulf Stream off Delaware, Virginia and Maryland, returning to their traditional winter sites when mature.

An important calving and breeding area in the northeast Atlantic is the Cape Verde Islands. Females with young calves have been seen there, and songs have been recorded. The whales arrive in December, with the peak of activity occurring in March and April. Females calve in Mordiera Bay off the southwest shores of Sal, and in Bahia Sal Rei on the western side of Boa Vista. A photo-ID programme has recently established that at least one of the Cape Verde whales heads for Iceland to feed in the summer, the first evidence of a migration route from Cape Verde to Europe in the northeast Atlantic.

Humpback whales are sighted occasionally off western coasts of the British Isles, and recordings of whale song have been made between October and March, when animals have been moving southwestwards. Whether these are en route to or from the West Indies in the western Atlantic or the Cape Verde Islands in the eastern Atlantic is unknown. One of the few positive photo-ID re-sightings in waters around the British Isles was of a young humpback that travelled 746 miles (1,200km) from County Cork in southwest Ireland to Dutch North Sea waters off the Netherlands in the summer of 2007

Since 1990 humpback whales have been appearing more often in both the western and eastern basins of the Mediterranean Sea, where previously they had been rare. In 2001, for example, a solitary humpback was spotted in the Bay of Tolo on the eastern coast of the Peloponnese, another was sighted in 2002 in the strait between Lefkada and Meganisi islands in the Ionian Sea, and in 2004 yet another was seen off Corfu, Greece. In 2003, a floating dead humpback was found off the Syrian coast. Elsewhere, they have been seen off the French and Italian coasts, including in the Adriatic.

Young whales get lost in the Baltic. A humpback christened 'Valpuri' (a female whose Finnish name comes from an 8th century German saint) crossed the Baltic Sea in 1978, and another appeared in the northern part of the Gulf of Bothnia in July 2006. The earlier whale, thought to be a juvenile, was in the area for six months and died, presumably of starvation.

Southern hemisphere

In the southern hemisphere, humpbacks spend the summer at feeding grounds around the Antarctic, with whales found as far south as the Antarctic Peninsula and the Weddell Sea. They migrate to winter breeding grounds in waters closer to the equator. The southeast Pacific population journeys between Costa Rica and the Antarctic, the longest known migration of any whale (see Migration north p.162).

In the South Atlantic, whales are seen off the west coast of Africa in winter, and along the east coast of South America, the latter travelling to and from breeding sites off Brazil. Humpbacks from the South Sandwich Islands in summer, for example, have been identified off Brazil in winter.

Newly discovered breeding sites have been identified in waters off Gabon in West Africa and in the Baie d'Antongil, on the northeast coast of Madagascar, the latter a nursery also for a large number of shark species. In each case, mothers have been seen with newborn calves, and humpback songs have been recorded.

In the Indian Ocean, whales are present in winter from East Africa to the Horn of Africa. The population of humpbacks in the Arabian Sea is unusual in that it seems not to migrate at all, but remains in tropical waters all year round.

In waters close to the South Pacific Island of Tonga is a small population of humpbacks that are the least known. It is thought they over-winter in Antarctic waters to the south of New Zealand and Australia, but their migration route is little known. Other populations pass the winter in waters around Samoa, the Cook Islands and New Caledonia.

Recent satellite tagging studies in the Cook Islands, supported by Greenpeace, revealed that the whales were moving generally in a westerly direction, towards American Samoa in the north and Tonga in the south, indicating at least part of the migration route of this population. Whales similarly tagged in the southern lagoon of New Caledonia moved either to a reef area to the southeast or north along the coast before heading west to the Chesterfield Islands in the Coral Sea early in the winter. Later in the season they headed south to Norfolk Island or the north coast of New Zealand, presumably on their way to the Antarctic, separate from the east Australian sub-population.

Australian whales head for the Antarctic in summer, but in the winter they form two discrete populations – one on the east coast and the other on the west. Only a few females from each generation travel between the two. During the latter days of commercial whaling for humpbacks in the southern hemisphere an imbalance appeared in the Australian population. During the late 1950s, humpbacks moving along the west coast were significantly younger than those travelling the east coast.

Surface behaviour

Humpback whales spend about 90 per cent of their time underwater, where it is difficult and expensive to study their behaviour. This means the real challenge for whale biologists is to ascertain what is going on down below by studying what goes on at the surface.

Breaching

The 10 per cent of behaviour that is observable can be very dramatic. Whales, and humpback whales especially, perform a variety of highly physical movements, such as breaching, lunging, lobtailing, slapping and spyhopping. The most dramatic is breaching, when at least 40 per cent and often up to 90 per cent of the animal's body is clear of the water. The whale travels rapidly below and parallel to the surface, and then bends upwards to leave the water at an angle of about 30–35° to the horizontal (although whales have been seen to breach at angles up to 70°). It then twists in mid-air so that its flank or back crashes back into the water. It rarely belly-flops, although whales observed by Hal Whitehead, of Dalhousie University, at Silver Bank in the West Indies belly-flopped 20 per cent of the time, with belly flops tending to follow belly-flops.

It has been calculated that the 40ft (12m) long whale must be travelling at a minimum of 15 knots (17mph or 27km/h) to achieve take-off, the whale pumping with its tail no more than three or four times to reach its maximum speed. Breaching tends to be carried out in bouts. Once a whale has started to breach, it is likely to continue to do so many times, and when the wind gets up, whales seem to breach more often.

143

Whales sometimes have near misses, almost mid-air collisions. They breach side-by-side, seemingly trying to land in the same patch of sea. Why they do this is unknown. Indeed, the reason for breaching is unknown, but the whale uses up a considerable amount of energy doing it so it must have a function other than 'being fun'. Scientists have speculated on what might be going on. Whales breach in social situations, indicating it might have a communication function. It might be used as a sign of rank or status, or it might indicate that a whale is present, ready and waiting – a kind of roll call. It might also warn of danger, or help coordinate a social event, such as cooperative feeding. It might frighten fish, or simply be a way of shifting irritating external parasites. Calves breach to exercise growing muscles, much like a kid goat or lamb leaping; it is a part of growing up. Whales tend to breach if they are within 6 miles (10km) of another whale breaching, and they might breach 50 times in a row. The first breach is the biggest, subsequent breaches becoming gradually less energetic as the whale tires, often no more than head lunges by the end of a breaching session. One of the longest sessions so far recorded was by a humpback at Silver Bank in the West Indies. It breached 130 times in 75 minutes.

Whales often breach when a liaison with another whale starts or finishes, or when a task is completed. They have also been seen to breach when a group of sharks swims past. Maybe it has multiple uses. The whale is showing its maximum power to other whales, which would be useful during courtship, challenging rivals or any circumstance where a show of strength is needed. Whatever the reason for breaching, scientists consider it an 'honest signal', something a whale cannot fake. And whatever the whale is saying, it is said with considerable emphasis.

Lunging

A leap is described as a 'lunge' when less than 40 per cent of the whale leaves the water. It is shown during feeding bouts on the summer feeding grounds and during fights at winter breeding sites. It might take the form of a 'chin slap', usually an aggressive display. If a group of males threatens another male, it will raise its chin above the water and bring it down heavily on the surface. It gives the same display to approaching killer whales, an attempt to intimidate them and scare them off. It might also present this display to boats.

Lobtailing and peduncle

Lobtailing is also forceful. The whale lifts its tail out of the water and brings it back down with a loud 'thwack'. It can be heard underwater from several hundred yards away, and, like breaching, is performed many times in a row. There is speculation that this is also a form of non-vocal communication, possibly a sign of aggression or a signal indicating a particular whale is present. It might also be used to concentrate fish by frightening them into tight, defensive balls, or as a defence against predators. A whale's tail is a powerful weapon.

A peduncle throw is a blocking manoeuvre using the tail. The peduncle is the stock joining the tail flukes to the body. In this manoeuvre the whale pivots using its pectoral fins, converting its forward motion into a tight turn. At the same time its head is thrust downward and the peduncle is lifted out of the water and pushed sideways. Males may use it several times to thwart a rival, and females will use it to deter any escort she considers a nuisance. Researchers have also seen peduncle throws directed at whale-watching boats that have approached too close to a whale.

Flipper slapping

Humpbacks turn on their side or their back and slap their huge flippers against the sea's surface, in a less forceful, even languid, display, known also as 'pec-slapping' or pectoral fin slapping. A whale might be at the surface and turn on its back and roll backwards and forwards, slapping first with one fin and then the other, even though there is not another whale nearby. Then, some distance away, another whale will begin to slap, and then another; so, pec-slapping also appears to be some form of non-vocal communication.

The fin or flipper itself has the same structure as the human hand, with the same bones present. They give the humpback exceptional manoeuvrability for such a large animal. Using them like a pair of independent rudders, it can negotiate tight turns, roll the body and swim in great loops. When swimming at speed they are held flat against the body.

In a manoeuvre that Dan Salden, founder of the Hawaii Whale Research Foundation, has called the 'crucifix block', a male whale will get ahead of its opponent, spread out its pectoral fins on either side like brakes and stop suddenly to form a barrier between the competitor and the female.

Spyhopping

Spyhopping is when a whale raises the front part of its body vertically clear of the water and holds it there momentarily, maybe for several minutes, before sinking back down. It is quite different to breaching and lunging in being a gentle manoeuvre. The eye is often clear of the water, so it is thought that this is one way the whale checks out things on the surface, such as a whale-watching boat approaching or the arrival of potential predators.

All these highly visible patterns of behaviour are seen both on the summer feeding sites in higher latitudes and the winter breeding sites at lower latitudes. In the northern Pacific, a key breeding site is the Hawaii Archipelago.

Hawaii winter breeding sites

How long whales have been coming to Hawaii is unknown. Veteran whale and dolphin researcher Louis Herman, founder of the Kewalo Basin Marine Mammal Laboratory and President of The Dolphin Institute, looked at the cultural and historical records of the islanders prior to Captain James Cook's visit in 1778, and he could find few references to humpback whales. People reached the islands first in about AD 400, but as they had no written language, information was sought from oral histories, legends and archaeological finds, such as petroglyphs, Herman concluded that either the whales were not present in significant numbers before the 18th century or the islanders ignored them.

However, Hawaiian folklore and legend encompasses almost every element of the natural world, especially life in and around the oceans, so it is unlikely Hawaiians would overlook a creature as large as a whale. In fact, they have not. The Hawaiian name for 'whale' is *Kohola* or *Palaoa* (older word), the body form of the god *Kanaloa*, and its blow is *ha*, meaning 'breath of life', but these words refer generally not to the humpback, but to the sperm whale. Sperm whale teeth were prized ornaments. They were carved into a tongue shape, the *lei palaoa* or whale pendant, and hung from braided strands of human hair to form a whale tooth necklace, the *lei niho palaoa*. The *Ali'i* (chiefs) of high rank were permitted to wear it, the tongue shape of the pendant signifying some one who speaks with authority.

One petroglyph at Palaoa Hill on the island of Lana'i, however, looks remarkably like a leaping humpback with a man riding on his back, possibly the son of the priest Maku who had been playing on a whale carcass that suddenly came to life. The

147

hill is a vantage point overlooking areas of the sea where hump-back whales are regularly seen. And throughout the island there are names of places and winds reflecting the presence of humpback whales, such as *Koholalele*, meaning 'leaping whale', a clear reference to a humpback, and *Laeonakohola* is the 'cape of whales' on the island of Kaho'olawe, from where humpback whales are seen as they travel through the islands. On Big Island, *Pu'ukohola Heiau* is the temple on the hill of whales, from where humpback whales can be seen in the sea below, at least in the winter months.

So, it could be that the humpback was revered to such an extent it was rarely spoken about except by special people who did not share the knowledge with others, and so it has been lost from the oral history. The other explanation is that humpbacks were not considered important, as they were absent for half the year, and featured very little in the oral history. A third explanation is that the humpback is a relatively recent visitor, some say as recently as 200 years ago, perhaps the result of whaling and other manmade pressures in other parts of the Pacific, or the consequence of a shift in water masses that affected the whales' preferred water temperature, or simply the result of dispersion from another area.

By the 19th century, however, Hawaii's whales were well and truly 'discovered', and it was not long after Captain Cook's ill-fated second visit to the islands that the whalers arrived. The first ships – the *Balena* of New Bedford and the *Equator* of Nantucket – hove into view on 17 September 1819, anchoring at Lahaina. They were not there for humpbacks, but were prospecting for sperm whales. The following year they discovered sperm whales in the sea between Hawaii and Japan, and by 1846 there were more than 736 ships taking on provisions and freshwater for sorties into the western Pacific. It was the main industry of the islands.

It was not long, therefore, before whalers began to notice that humpbacks were close to shore in the Hawaiian Islands during the winter. Some of the sperm whalers assisted small shore-based operators to catch them, but at that time humpback oil was less in demand than sperm whale oil, so the industry never really took off. By the beginning of the 20th century, whaling operations had moved to Arctic and Antarctic waters, and the humpbacks took a pounding, not in Hawaii but while on their feeding grounds off Alaska. Their oil became as valuable as the sperm whales', and by the 1960s the North Pacific population had been reduced from an estimated 15,000 whales (best guess) before commercial whaling started to little more than 1,500 whales.

Curiously, any surviving whales in Hawaiian waters went unnoticed until 1975, when Louis Herman brought them to the attention of the scientific community.

Whales arrive for winter

Each year, Hawaii's humpbacks appear offshore round about October. Local people welcome them. When the first whale is spotted the word is out – 'the whales are here!' They are often spotted for the first time in a stretch of sea between McGregor Point and Kamaiki Point, known to researchers as the 'humpback highway'. Females without calves tend to arrive first, some as early as mid-September, followed by mothers with yearlings. Immature whales are next, including yearlings abandoned on the feeding grounds and juveniles of both sexes. Mature males make up the next wave, followed by 'resting' females. Bringing up the rear are late pregnant females. They trickle in over the autumn and winter months, the pace of activity increasing in December, and peaking in late January and February.

Why they go to Hawaii at all is a bit of a mystery, because

there is little food for humpback whales. Scientists have a pretty good idea about what they do when they get there, but not why they went in the first place. Some scientists suggest they visit Hawaii in winter because it is a safe refuge in a vast ocean, and the subtropical waters are perfect for newly born calves. Adult whales drop their calves, court and mate in the lee of the islands, sheltered from the powerful ocean waves that roll in from the northeast and are whipped into a fury by the trade winds.

Others suggest that they have a need for shallow submarine banks. In Hawaii, for example, in the Penguin Bank area to the southwest of Laau Point and Ilio Point on Molokai, the water averages 200ft (60m) deep; and in the area surrounded by the four islands Maui, Lanai, Molokai and Kaho'olawe, it is no more than 263ft (80m) deep.

The same is true in the western Atlantic. Researchers have noticed that the majority of humpbacks at Silver Bank, Navidad Bank and other areas frequented by humpbacks in the West Indies, are less than 200ft (60m) deep; likewise, humpbacks in the South Pacific are found mainly over shallow banks and reefs. Underwater topography or bathymetry, it seems, is far more important to humpback whales than whether they are in coastal waters or not. One other common factor is that all the wintering sites are close to latitude 20° North or South.

In Hawaii, female whales probably go to different islands depending on what they are doing. Females with calves tend to go to the shallower waters of Maui, while those same females when without calves go to Big Island. It seems different parts of the archipelago are used in different reproductive states.

Some whales do not stop when they reach the traditional assembly points, such as Penguin Bank and the Four Islands area, but island hop from the big islands in the east through to the Kauai–Niihau region. As the Hawaiian whale population has increased, the whales have begun to spill over into areas in the lee of these more northwesterly islands in the archipelago. During the season, the peak of activity in each place is progressively later the further west the island, indicating that the whales are possibly using the prevailing clockwise surface currents in the northern Pacific to swing round from Alaska to their winter residencies in the northwest of the archipelago.

Winter fast

From the moment they leave the feeding grounds to the time they return, humpbacks do not feed or feed very little. They rely on vast amounts of fat in the form of blubber, which was put on during the summer months, to see them through. Pregnant females maximise food intake by being last to leave the feeding grounds, for when they become lactating females with calves they lose weight rapidly. During commercial whaling days, records show that pregnant females yielded twice the quantity of oil as late-lactating mothers with calves. The whalers knew they would get large quantities of oil at the end of the summer feeding season, but very little oil at the end of the winter season. A female with calf loses about a third of her bodyweight from the end of the feeding season to her return to feed the following spring.

Most whales on the winter grounds are unlikely to feed for several months. However, some observers cruising around Lanai and over Penguin Bank have photographed humpbacks that appeared to be feeding at their winter breeding sites. Fierce currents run between Lanai and Maui, where large shoals of fish run. According to local fishermen, the whales are spaced out and fish for Pacific chub mackerel generally before sunrise. The mackerel arrive to feed on newly hatched prawns and the whales take advantage of a quick snack. In March 1989, Dan Salden spotted a solitary sub-adult male feeding on mackerel between Lanai and Maui. It made a feeding lunge at a shoal,

151

appearing vertically out of the water with its throat pleats distended and its mouth partially open.

Winter predators

There are generally fewer predators in the winter sites than on the summer feeding grounds. In Hawaiian waters, false killer whales and tiger sharks have been known to attack newborn calves and the sick or elderly, but these encounters are infrequent. Killer whales or orcas, including pods related to mammal-eating pods more usually seen in the Gulf of Alaska, have also been spotted in Hawaiian waters during at least nine months of the year. On one occasion orcas were seen feeding on a humpback whale carcass, and another time they were spotted feeding on squid, but these sightings are also not common.

So, with little feeding and a relatively low level of predation, there is less need for humpback whales to form into groups while on the winter breeding sites. Increased alertness, communal defence, and safety in numbers are less essential in these subtropical waters, so any groups at this time of year tend to be small. Most whales tend to avoid others of their own kind, unless courting, mating or fighting for the right to do either.

Whale groups

Unlike many of the toothed whales, which seem to remain in family groups for life, humpbacks have shorter periods of social interaction with other humpbacks. Mothers and calves, remaining together for a year, are probably the longest associations. Cooperative-feeding groups may stay together for part or all of the summer and bachelor groups may sometimes form for short periods on the winter breeding grounds, but the social bonds are transient. In winter, humpback whales tend to be loners that seek the company of other humpbacks only occasionally.

152

On the winter breeding ground the basic social affiliation is a pair of whales. There are females with calves, females with males, and males with males, but never females with females. On the breeding grounds, a female with a calf will avoid another female with her calf. On the summer feeding grounds, however, females often get together with other females, and spend time together in the same feeding groups each year.

Competitive groups

In Hawaii, the most common grouping is a female, with or without a calf, together with an escort, known as a 'primary escort', often the largest and longest males. In humpback whale society, size matters. These giant escorts could be prospecting for a receptive female or guarding a recently mated one. No one is sure, for mating itself has yet to be witnessed. They generally swim alongside and below the mother, or mother and calf. In such a threesome, the male is not guarding his partner and offspring. Generally he is neither the calf's father nor the mother's regular partner, but a male patiently waiting for the female to be ready to mate.

At breeding sites, large boisterous groups of mainly males are also seen at the surface, especially at the peak times of sexual readiness between mid-February and mid-March. Scientists refer to them as 'competitive groups' in which a whole bunch of aggressive males, known as 'secondary escorts', attempt to oust the primary escort from his place alongside the female. It could be that the female chooses a mate on the basis of how long he can retain the primary escort position. So, understandably, the primary escort fights back, and he uses a series of moves that are increasingly violent. The least damaging are broadside displays, and these are followed in escalating intensity by underwater exhalations, head lunges (during which the throat is sometimes expanded), physical displacement and charge-strikes.

Encrustations of barnacles growing on the whale's snout often cause blood to be spilled, and sometimes whales die.

On one occasion in 1996, a group of competing whales was seen to be behaving normally by passengers on a tourist whale-watching boat, but they began to notice something was wrong. One of the whales had floated to the surface and was floating there on its side. At first people thought the whale was about to give birth, but then they realised it was not breathing. The skipper radioed for help and several research boats raced to the scene. Divers dropped into the water and were able to confirm that the whale was, indeed, dead, but while they were examining the body the strangest thing happened.

They spotted a large bull humpback about 80–90ft (24–27m) down, and it was heading for the surface like a guided missile in slow motion. It swam to the dorsal side of the dead whale and wrapped its pectoral fins around it. When it got no reaction, it let go, and dived below, only to resurface and do the same thing again. It did this time and again for several hours. The scientists were at a loss to explain it. Some suggested it could be helping behaviour, others thought that it might be dominance behaviour, similar to the way bull elephants will mount a dying competitor. In videos taken at the time, the living whale is seen to extrude its penis, so dominance could well be an explanation.

The primary escort is usually larger than most of the secondary escorts, for their gang often includes juvenile and sub-adult males who are learning how to fight, and they either remain on the periphery of the group, watching and learning, or they do it the hard way and end up bloodied and battered.

If the female is selecting a mate on the basis of how escorts perform, it is she who appears to set the pace. It could be that she prolongs the fighting and avoids mating too early by swimming rapidly, sometimes belly up, and by swatting suitors with her long pectoral fins. If and when she makes a selection, the honour of being primary escort is short-lived, no more than a few hours. DNA tests confirm that there are no long-term relationships. Different males have fathered calves born to the same female in different years.

The watching scientists sometimes observe unexpected behaviour at this time. For example, female without calf, which had recently arrived from Alaska, was immediately surrounded by a large group of males competing for her attention. It looked like a female about to get pregnant. However, when spotted again two weeks later she had given birth, so the males were unlikely to have mated with her. Why then the males persisted with their courtship fight is another mystery.

In Hawaii, females tend not to gain escorts until after 7am, and boisterous behaviour, such as fin and tail slapping, breaching and head lunging, is most evident after 9.30 every morning. The peak in male fighting is in the afternoon. This violent competition between males is probably because the sex ratio of males to females at the winter sites is skewed in favour of females. When the largest number of females is available for mating, it is estimated that there are two males to every female. With pregnant females leaving early for the feeding grounds and some females not visiting the breeding sites at all the ratio is even more skewed; hence the fighting.

Songs and singers

Escort duty alternates with singing, one of the most evocative aspects of humpback whale behaviour. Herman Melville wrote in *Moby Dick* that 'the whale has no voice', but the reality is that the humpback whale not only has a voice but an unexpectedly melodic one. Sailors once told how, when resting in their hammocks, they could hear strange and eerie melodies through the bottom of their wooden boats and ships. It is not hard to imagine that these sounds could be mistaken for a chorus of dead colleagues. Maybe Homer's Sirens, who tried to lure Odysseus's men to their deaths, were in fact singing humpback whales.

On the coast of southwest Ireland, the ballad *Port na bPúcaí*, meaning 'Music of the Fairies', is linked to humpback whales on their southward migration. Legend holds that three fishermen from Inishvickillane Island were rowing their currach when they heard melodic sounds coming through the hull. One of them took up his fiddle and played along with the sounds, thought to have been the songs of fairies.

Only male humpbacks sing. They sing at winter sites and on migration, and occasionally on the feeding grounds. The reasons for singing, however, are not at all clear, and many suggestions have been made. Song could be a sexual advertisement, males singing to impress and attract a mate in the way that some birds do. It could also synchronise ovulation in females. Singing might be a means of spacing out males in the sea, or prospecting for cooperative bachelor partnerships in order to overthrow a female's primary escort, or it could be a way for males to assess the strengths and weakness of other males, in a way similar to the roaring of red deer stags. Several researchers have drawn attention to the fact that the singing whales are spaced out in the ocean like prairie chickens at a lek or bullfrogs at a pond, but as females seem not to be attracted to the songs, it is unlikely to be a conventional lek. Non-singing whales tend to be no more that 1.2 miles (2km) apart but singers, on average, are spaced 3.1 miles (5km) apart, and they sing over both shallow and deep water. The males, though, are not territorial so it would not be a classic lek mating system, but what scientists have called a 'floating lek'.

A function favoured by veteran whale song researcher Jim Darling, founder of the West Coast Whale Research Foundation (Pacific Wildlife Foundation), is that song facilitates some kind of male social ordering. Much emphasis has been placed on the aggressive behaviour of males in competitive groups, but this is not the whole picture. Males also appear to cooperate or form coalitions or liaisons. One observer watching whales in Hawaiian waters reported how two other males joined a singing whale, and the three of them joined with a competitive group attempting to displace a primary escort from his position next to female.

The songs are very loud. Divers in the water close to singing whales tell of their entire body vibrating and their ears hurting. Singers can be heard from considerable distances away, low frequencies clearly audible from up to 50 miles (80km) when acoustic conditions are good. The whales might also use special conduits in the ocean, where different water densities funnel especially low-pitched sounds for transmitting over even greater distances, perhaps for hundreds of miles. The song is not produced omnidirectionally, but the sound appears to be focused. This implies that the singer is either finding places in the ocean where the sound will transmit best or aiming its sound beam at a particular target.

Whatever the reason for it and whatever the way it is generated, transmitted and attenuated, humpback whale song is dynamic. It evolves constantly throughout the season, and all the whales in a particular population sing the same song, seemingly achieved by vocal mimicry. Whales in Hawaii, for example all sing the same song, and even those in Mexico similar very similar variations.

In a study of humpback whale songs in 1989, songs from Hawaii, Japan and Mexico were compared. Of seven themes identified, three themes appeared in all three regions. In addition, Hawaii and Mexico had five themes in common, Hawaii and Japan shared four themes, and Mexico and Japan shared three themes. It indicates that there is some acoustic

157

contact between whales in the three winter grounds during some part of their migratory cycle.

The northern Pacific song, however, differs completely from the song sung by whales in the northwest Atlantic or Indian Ocean, for example. And whales off the Cape Verde Islands sing songs with similarities to those over-wintering in the West Indies, suggesting that there is a link between those two stocks. The rate of song change varies in different locations. Humpbacks off Bermuda change their song entirely over five seasons, while in Australia they take no more than two seasons.

Also, when returning from their summer feeding grounds, singers pick up the last version of the song that they sang the previous year. While most songs are sung on the winter breeding grounds, songs have been recorded on the summer feeding grounds, especially towards the end of the summer, when the whales are preparing for their migration south.

The song is like bird song, but slowed down. It has several themes, each composed of two or three repeatable phrases, which, in turn, are composed of individual units of sound. Themes are sung in a fixed sequence, the entire song cycle lasting for between five and 20 minutes. The singing session, however, can go on for hours, the singer ending a song and then going back to the beginning to start it again, and again.

Singers are usually alone, often hanging in the water with their head down at a depth of 50–100ft (15–30m). A few sing while actively swimming. Other males approach singers. Smaller males sometimes sidle up and appear to watch and listen, as do other singers who stop singing and join singers. They are known as 'joiners'. Sometimes, the joiner and singer team up and swim away together, and maybe interact with a female; other times the joiner will leave and the singer continues to sing, or the singer will stop singing altogether and leave. Females rarely approach singers.

Social sounds

Humpbacks also make other social sounds. Competitive male groups make raucous sounds when fighting, and these might act like a beacon for other males in the area. Often researchers have seen bulls making a beeline for competitive groups or male-female pairs, from considerable distances away, distances over which they would be unable to see their target but they could certainly hear it.

Mothers and calves exchange sounds, the calves producing repeated low-frequency burps, which increase in intensity, and higher frequency squeals. The sounds are aimed primarily at the mother. They also produce bubble streams, a form of alarm to alert the mother. The females are thought to make social sounds at even lower frequencies. These are sounds that we cannot hear but we sometimes 'feel', known as infrasounds. Whales also produce loud fishing calls when feeding co-operatively on their summer feeding grounds.

In playback experiments in Hawaii, researchers played recordings of humpback song, female feedings calls from Alaska, social sounds, or nothing. The whales did not approach the boat when song was played, but they reacted strongly to feeding calls, approaching the boat like torpedoes. It is as if the call is a 'dinner bell', which tells all that there is food to be had. This is one hypothesis. It might also be that bull whales are recognising these feedings calls as being from females, so they rush to the source.

This dependence on sound for most of their natural behaviour means that humpback whales (and other species of whales) are susceptible to interference from manmade noise. Various forms of noise pollution, whether from engines, propellers, explosions from seismic exploration or military sonar installations, are in the sound spectrum used by whales. It is like people in a bar trying to talk against very loud music. The sounds are deafening and prevent vocal communication.

Reproduction: facts and figures

Reproduction is highly seasonal. Data from the southern hemisphere during the days of commercial whaling shows that male testes grow significantly during the winter, with sperm maturing (spermatogenesis) during the austral winter, in late July and August. In the northern hemisphere, this occurs six months later, in late January and February, although the time of most courtship activity in Hawaii is the first two weeks in March. Female ovulation is timed to coincide with the peak of male sperm production. Even so, in the northern Pacific ovulation peaks during February, but occurs anytime between January and April. Most females ovulate just once, giving males a relatively brief window of opportunity, although a few females have been known to ovulate twice or even three times during the season.

Females reach sexual maturity as early as five years of age in the North Atlantic, males up to five years later. In southeast Alaska, females have not been seen with calves until they are closer to 11 years old. Females conceive in the winter, and conception is thought to take place on the way to or at the winter breeding sites. Nobody has witnessed the event. Gestation is 11–12 months, so any mating taking place in one year will result in a birth the following year. Although scientists have observed a grey whale and a sperm whale birth, researchers have yet to witness the birth of a humpback calf.

On 11 January 1994, however, tourists on a commercial whale-watching boat about 985ft (300m) off the Lahaina shoreline watched what they believed to have been a humpback birth. They saw a lone whale that was active at the surface. It then dived below for about eight minutes and returned to the surface accompanied by a 12ft (3.6m)-long calf with curled tips to its tail flukes. No other whales were in the area at the time. About 15 minutes later, they noticed a large placenta floating in the water. Similar evidence of births, such as pieces of afterbirth floating on the surface, has been found close to probable nursery sites – the shallow bays and coves on the southern coasts of Hawaii's larger islands, especially Maui.

Babies are suckled on milk with 60 per cent fat for a little over 10 months. Calves put on weight, and continue to feed on their mother's milk in the feeding grounds, although they start on solids at six or seven months and are usually weaned before or during the return journey to Hawaii. Separation occurs after a year, when yearlings are 26–30ft (8–9m) in length. Occasionally, youngsters separate from their mother in the feeding grounds, but most go their separate ways when the mother and yearling return to their winter sites. About 80 per cent of whales survive their first year.

There are, however, some years when calves without mothers are seen around Hawaii. Whether the mothers died while giving birth or abandoned unhealthy calves and returned early to the feeding ground is unknown. For example, scientists spotted a male calf without a mother that was trying to obtain milk from any whale that passed by. Humpbacks, though, are not into 'auntying'. They will not nurse each other's offspring. Nevertheless, the youngster was spotted again several weeks later alive and well, suggesting that these youngsters are more robust and more enterprising than was first thought.

Mothers tend to have babies every two to three years, but there are a few that give birth and conceive in the same year. These whales are pregnant, lactating and fasting all at the same time. In Alaska's Glacier Bay, three females have turned up with a new calf in successive years, and one female has given birth three years in a row. If a female whale should live to 70 years old, she is likely to have at least 15 calves during her lifetime.

In Hawaii, calving, courtship and mating continue throughout the winter and through to spring, after which the procession of whales returns to its summer feeding grounds. Newly pregnant females and resting females head off first, followed by immature animals of both sexes. Mature males go next, with lactating mothers and recently born calves the last to leave. The tail-enders will have set out by June.

Migration north

Hawaii's humpbacks travel across the entire North Pacific basin to traditional feeding grounds along the northern rim of the ocean. They go to waters off British Columbia, southeast Alaska, the Gulf of Alaska, and the Aleutian Islands. Some also head for the southern Bering Sea, Russia's Kamchatka Peninsula and the Farallon Islands off San Francisco. The fastest whales make it to southeast Alaska from Maui in a month-and-a-half, and stay for four to five months. The shortest recorded migration was during the southward movement when an individual that had been feeding in Sitka Sound, southeast Alaska, turned up on the northwest coast of Hawaii just 39 days later. It must have travelled at an average speed of 2.95mph (4.7km/h) over a distance of 2,760 miles (4,440km).

Initial satellite tracking studies by Oregon State University have shown that some of Hawaii's whales head directly to feeding grounds off Alaska and British Columbia, while others travel due north to the Aleutian Islands chain. One animal in particular arrived in the Aleutians, made a left turn and headed for Kamchatka, Russia. Another went to Canada's Queen Charlotte Islands before moving north to feed in southeast Alaska.

In a study of six whales tagged off Kauai, Hawaii, one

individual travelled a short 155 miles (250km) inter-island hop to Oahu in four days, and another visited Penguin Bank and Four Islands, covering 510 miles (820km) in 10 days. On the spring migration, three whales on independent headings set a north-northeasterly course for the Gulf of Alaska, and a female with a calf covered 416 miles (670km) in 4.5 days, which means the entire journey in a straight line could be completed in less than a month.

While most of the whales in the northern hemisphere are moving generally away from the equator and towards the pole, the humpbacks in the southern hemisphere are doing the opposite. This means that whales in the northern and southern sectors of the Pacific and Atlantic oceans rarely meet. Their annual migrations are out of sync. After spending the southern summer feeding in the Southern Ocean, close to the Antarctic, the southern hemisphere whales are heading north to their breeding sites in the tropics and subtropics.

It was once thought that humpbacks do not cross the equator, but there is at least one group that does so. Whales travelling along the Pacific coast of South America follow the cool Humboldt Current, so they have to travel beyond the equator to find warm waters suitable for calving. Humpbacks seem to prefer water with a temperature of about 70–82°F (21–28°C), and this they find off the coast of Costa Rica. Their journey from the Antarctic takes roughly 160 days, and they cover a distance of at least 5,288 miles (8,510km), the longest migration undertaken by any mammal on Earth (pushing grey whales into second place).

A few whales from the North Pacific population, however, also migrate to Costa Rica. They are probably feeding off the coast of Washington, Oregon and California, returning to Drake Bay in Costa Rica to breed. As whales have been seen in Costa Rican waters all year round, it is remotely possible that whales from the northern hemisphere are encountering those from the south. Genetic studies indicate that there was probably interbreeding in the past, and it is in Central American waters that it was likely to have happened.

Wherever they live, all these whales must know where they are and where they are going, and the signs are that they use the Earth's magnetic field. Whales, like pigeons and tuna, have small particles of magnetite (iron oxide) embedded in the dura mater covering of the anterior part of the brain. Like miniature magnets, these might orientate to the Earth's magnetic field, providing the whale with an inbuilt 'compass'. The magnetic field strength varies from place to place on the Earth's surface, with variations influenced by local geography, so the whales also have a map. Lines of magnetic intensity can be drawn on a map just like the contours of a conventional map, so magnetic hills and valleys could help guide the whales on their migration.

This is all speculation for the moment, but further evidence comes from stranding studies. Whales and ocean-going dolphins tend to strand where low-strength areas of the magnetic field intersect the coast. It is as if the whales were going along on automatic pilot, a safe bet in the open ocean, but a liability in inshore waters. They are taken unawares, and suddenly find themselves stranded in shallow water on an outgoing tide. Humpbacks and other whales, however, could be using areas of low-intensity magnetic fields to find their way across the ocean.

There is also speculation that the very low frequency calls humpback and other whales make could be used as an echolocation system. Sound travels four-and-half times faster in water than in air and low-pitched sounds travel great distances underwater, so instead of interrogating the sea immediately ahead, like dolphins do, the sound could be bouncing off islands, peninsulas, seamounts and other distant landmarks.

They might also be 'talking' to other whales heading the same way. In this way more experienced whales, which know the way, might indicate the route to younger, naïve whales.

The ocean is not a 'silent world' as the title of Jacques-Yves Cousteau's classic book would have us believe. It is actually filled with sound, and two sounds in particular puzzled scientists. They were a 'boing' sound and a very low frequency 20Hz signal. Both sounds had been picked up by military sonar and heard by submarine crews since the 1950s but their source was a mystery until research early in this decade. The boing turned out to be made by minke whales, the smallest of the baleen whales. The research showed that minke whale signals consist of a brief pulse followed by a longer call that sweeps down from 100Hz to 60 or 90Hz depending on the location, and emitted at intervals of 28 seconds. In other animals, such as bats, such a frequency-modulated signal is used in echolocation, the sweep being a way of obtaining more information about the target. Could minke whales be using the signal in the same way?

The 20Hz sound was equally bewildering until scientists used large underwater microphone arrays on the seabed and with these they were able to triangulate the sound back to its source, which turned out to be fin whales, the second largest whale after the blue whale. Fin whales make two types of sound, both of which are inaudible to people. There are sounds of one-second duration with a frequency sweep from 23 to 18Hz, and a second sound pitched at a constant frequency of 18–20Hz with an 800-millisecond duration. The sounds are emitted as pulses that last for up to half-an-hour, and when speeded up they sound like a short 'moo'.

Research in the Gulf of California (Sea of Cortez) indicates that one function of these 20Hz sounds is to attract a mate. Males emit the sounds when they find dense patches of food. When the females arrive to investigate, it is thought courtship and mating occurs. The whales appear to be communicating with other whales in a loose herd that is spread out across the ocean, and they are doing so with some of the lowest and most powerful sounds in nature, low-pitched sounds that are capable of propagating for many miles through the water. The frequency shift of one of the signals is further evidence for whole ocean basin navigation – a low-frequency echolocation system. With this whales could identify, say, an island by its size and shape from hundreds of miles away.

Feeding

Humpbacks are baleen whales, which means they have 250–450 baleen plates instead of teeth. The plates are made of keratin, the same substance that makes hair and fingernails. They are in two rows along the upper jaw, the size and shape varying between whale species. The humpback's baleen is about 25in (64cm) long, the blue whale 40 inches (100cm) long and the bowhead a massive 15ft (4.6m) long. They hang down from the upper jaw and they grow throughout a whale's life, which is just as well because they continually fray at the ends. The inner surface of the plates is also frayed, like combs of thick, coarse hair, and plates overlap to form a continuous mat that is used to filter out food from the mouthfuls of water they engulf when feeding. They work like a sieve.

Humpbacks are also rorquals, from the Latin meaning 'ruby-throat', which refers to the throat pleats that enable the humpback to expand its throat like an accordion so it is able to take in an even larger mouthful of water and food. The large tongue presses against the roof of the mouth, and forces the water out through the baleen. The food is trapped inside and swallowed.

As they feed mainly on their summer grounds, they need to maximise their food intake to be able to survive the rest of the year. They must feed almost continuously, and they have several feeding strategies to help them obtain the calories.

Humpbacks are technically 'lungers', in that they trap krill or small fish against the surface or within a trap and lunge into them with their mouths open. The jaws have especially elastic ligaments, enabling the lower jaw to open more than 90°. This differs from right whales and bowhead whales, which are 'skimmers'. They ease themselves through the water skimming off food as they swim. For humpbacks, feeding itself occurs mainly in higher latitudes, such as Alaska's Alexander Archipelago, where the summer bloom of phytoplankton gives rise to a well-stocked food chain that includes small fish and krill, abundant food for whales. Whales eat whatever is plentiful, and adopt different feeding methods to collect it. In southeast Alaska, some whales eat mainly krill while others are feeding on schooling fish.

Fish feeders

The fish feeders tackle food that is difficult to catch, mainly herring in southeast Alaska. These fish are fast, zipping about at 10ft (3m) per second, so they could easily outmanoeuvre a large whale. Some humpbacks overcome this by acting together. They dive down to 100–150ft (30–45m) to get below herring swimming at 70–80ft (21–24m) and then drive the fish upwards, using an unusual type of net to contain them in one area. It is a behaviour and sophisticated form of tool use that was observed in the North Atlantic by Norwegian whaler Morten Andreas Ingebrigtsen in 1929, and later observed in the North Pacific by Charles and Virginia Jurasz in Glacier Bay, and by Cynthia D'Vincent of the Intersea Foundation in the Alexander Archipelago.

As the whales reach a depth of about 70ft (21m), one of the group begins to blow a huge rising curtain of bubbles, many

167

tens of yards across. It acts like a net – a bubblenet in which the herring are trapped within a gigantic rising cylinder of bubbles.

Whales tend to have the same feeding partners each year, and in the large cooperative feeding groups they become part of a team, often playing the same role in that team. One whale blows the bubble ring, another gives a feeding call, and others wave their flippers about so the bright white patches frighten the fish. They work in concert, in a carefully choreographed event to herd the fish to the surface.

Key to the fishing's effectiveness are more vocalisations, an aspect of whale research studied by Fred Sharpe and Sean Hanser of the Alaska Whale Research Foundation. They have discovered that sometimes, when two groups get together to herd an especially large shoal of herring, there is conflict about who is doing what. The social structure of the group changes – who will be the bubble-blower and who will be the caller, for instance. So the two groups appear to debate loudly, screaming at each other until a consensus is reached. They are unusually aggressive during these spats, and there are combinations of whales that just do not work well together. They are equally vociferous if an individual fouls up during the fishing, screaming what in the whale communication system can only be translated as 'you idiot!'.

The feeding call, with dominant frequencies at 390–550Hz, is similar to a short song in that it has phrases that are sung time and again in the same order. Unlike songs on the winter breeding grounds, the feeding call is the same every year, but each group of whales has its own distinctive call. It is especially raucous and so helps to frighten the fish into a defensive ball. This is a fine defence strategy when salmon or seals confront the fish. They can only pick off fish one by one. However, it is quite the wrong strategy to use with humpbacks that could swallow the fish ball in a single gulp.

The frequency of the sound is significant. These low-pitched sounds are at the very frequencies that laboratory studies have shown to be most effective in frightening fish and disrupting shoals. The calls can be short or long, separate groups having calls of different lengths, indicating the quality of the call is probably more important than its length. The sounds are also specialised. Only whales in southeast Alaska and British Columbia waters make them. They are not heard in any other parts of the world.

The herring do not try to escape through the bubbles so, with the whales below them waving their flippers, they head to the only free space available to them, close to the surface, just where the humpbacks want them. The surface is the best place to trap fish. It is like a blind alley. They cannot escape. When they try, they simply drop back into the sea.

At an unknown signal, the whales rise up through the centre of the cylinder of bubbles with their mouths open and throats expanding, and they take in great mouthfuls of fish and seawater. There is some pushing and shoving, but each time the whales surface, they come up in the same place in the group and with the same orientation. Whales in the middle surface vertically, while those at the sides surface laterally with their pectoral fins in the air. And each time they sound again, they dive down below in the same order.

In groups of cooperatively feeding humpbacks, one whale is often the most vociferous or will breach more often than the others, say, when the prey is thinning out or when killer whales approach. It was thought at first to be a matriarch, but later research discovered that both males and females could be team leaders, and they remained leaders during two decades of research. One such individual was 'Big Mama', in one of Sean Hanser's study groups. Big Mama had been very tolerant of mothers with calves, so they tended to join her group. Calves tend to get in the way, playing with the bubblenet or winding up in the middle of the surfacing whales, but Big Mama was not fazed by any of this. It revealed to Hanser's colleagues that, just like us, there are many characters with different personalities in humpback society. Big Mama, alas, has not been seen for a long while, so researchers believe she has gone to that 'great bubblenet in the sky'.

In southeast Alaska, about 1,000 whales move in and out of the area during the course of the summer, and 800 or so may try their hand at cooperative feeding. Only 50 unrelated individuals, however, are members of an elite cooperative feeding team. They feed in the Chatham Strait area of southeast Alaska, and they are like a well-drilled football squad. Each year the same whales perform the same tasks within each team. There are about a dozen specialised bubble-blowers and callers, for instance, and they are called upon to use their skills every year. Each, however, has its own technique for blowing bubbles. Some whales deputise, so that if one of the key players is not available the team can continue to feed. They blow more bubblenets per hour, mess up less and so capture more food each day than the more temporary groups elsewhere in the region. They also seldom change their prey for most of the season. These whales feed on herring and little else. When the herring thin out in late summer, most will hunt around for more shoals rather than switch to krill, but when the herring have gone to deeper water, they will take krill instead, always maximising their opportunities to feed before heading south.

In the summer of 1981, for example, C. Scott Baker and his colleagues from the Kewalo Basin Marine Mammal Laboratory in Hawaii observed a group of eight to 10 humpbacks bubblenet feeding in Frederick Sound. Two months later the same group were lunge feeding (see 'Krill feeders', below) in Chatham Strait about 85 miles (140km) away. Three years later the same group was seen at the same feeding locations.

Krill feeders

Krill are a different kettle of fish, so to speak. While whales fishing for herring are like wolves outsmarting and trapping prey, krill fishing is more like catching cows grazing on grass. Krill are shrimp-like euphausiid crustaceans that shun the light, so during the day they are deeper down. Whales feeding on krill up flukes and dive deep for six or seven minutes, then return to the surface, blow five or six times, and sound again.

The whales adopt any one of several strategies to concentrate them. They might blow small bubblenets, each resembling a long thin tube that can go down to 150ft (45m), much deeper than the shallow cooperative feeding bubblenets. They work in the same way, however, by frightening the krill into a tight swarm at the centre of the bubble cylinder. The whale then rises at a leisurely rate up through the tube, gathering the krill as it goes.

Whales also blow bubble clouds. The whale is able to adapt the size of its bubbles to the smaller size of the prey, and blow a fine mist. The tiny bubbles become locked under the exoskeleton of each tiny krill so the swarm is lifted and trapped against the surface where the whale can feed on them. Another method is flick feeding. The whale splashes the water with its tail and turns round to engulf anything caught in the disturbance.

When fishing krill or herring, the whales even use their long pectoral fins to herd the prey. There are usually white patches on the undersides of the flippers and these help frighten any prey attempting to dart out sideways back towards the whales' mouths.

In the Alexander Archipelago, one individual (or maybe

several – the researchers are not sure) rises vertically out of the water with its pectoral fins held out on either side, as if it is spyhopping. Water pouring from the sides and corners of its mouth indicate it has found a unique way of feeding, probably using gravity to accelerate the food down its throat. Another whale, described by William Dolphin when working on his PhD at Boston University, rose slowly until its pectoral flippers were at the surface and then it thrust them forward, throwing water ahead of itself. It then sank back down and lunged forward into the area where the spray landed. Dolphin called it a 'high vertical rise' or 'HVR'.

Herbert Hayes and colleagues from Shippensberg University were off Gloucester Harbour, Massachusetts, when they observed a further example of anomalous feeding. While other whales were using bubble clouds to trap sand lance that were thick in the water, one individual rose vertically out of the sea, exiting the surface with its mouth closed, the front third of its body out of the water. As it settled back down, its mouth parted slightly and it sank vertically, leaving a disturbance on the water similar to that left by a whale that has rolled. About 20 seconds later the whale reappeared at the same place with its mouth wide open. It is thought that when sinking, the whale created a reduced pressure zone that sucked in the sand lance, concentrating the prey in a column above its mouth. The whale then made a vertical lunge up through the sand lance, taking a mouthful of prey and seawater.

Most whales, however, use the lateral lunge technique. They usually turn onto their side and take long scoops through the swarm of krill. Sometimes a second and even a third whale join in, a technique known as 'echelon feeding'. Occasionally echelons of seven whales feeding synchronously have been seen. The first whale creates an upwelling that brings the krill to the surface, where the second and subsequent whales can take full advantage of the swirling effect. The affiliations are usually short-lived. Most whales do not form permanent teams from year to year as cooperative bubblenet feeders do, although some whales do have preferred feeding partners. Two whales in southeast Alaska, named 'Slinky' and 'Minister's Son', for example, have been seen together for 22 years. At feeding times, they are almost inseparable. A variation on the lateral lunge method is vertical lunge feeding, in which fish or krill are trapped against the surface and the whale lunges vertically upwards.

Nutritionally, herring is superior to krill. Weight for weight, herring delivers 50 per cent more calories than krill, so with only a few months to gather food, herring is an attractive target.

While Alaskan humpbacks and those in the Bering Sea take herring, capelin, sand lance, mackerel and krill, those feeding off the western Aleutians and south of the Amchitka Islands take large quantities of Atka mackerel and Pacific saury. North Atlantic whales add pollack to their diet. Mothers take their calves to preferred feeding areas, so their offspring are imprinted on that area.

Staying behind

When most of the whales head south in the autumn, some whales remain behind. They do not migrate; instead they spend the entire year on the feeding grounds. Ten whales have been recognised in the Sitka area of southeast Alaska, for example, that stay all year. This occurs not only in the North Pacific, but also in the northwest Atlantic and Southern Ocean. The ratio of males to females during the northward and southward migration along Australia's east coast is 2.4:1, which means that many females remain behind on the feeding grounds. The suggestion is that these could be immature animals, resting females or older whales that are no longer reproducing, so they do not bother to make a fruitless journey. While food is less abundant during the winter months, it is still there, and these characters take full advantage of it. Winter distribution in southeast Alaska appears to coincide with known concentrations of winter herring, such as the Lower Lynn Canal, Tenakee Inlet, Whale Bay, and Ketchikan.

As for the rest of the whales, they probably use up as much energy on migration as they would if swimming and feeding in one locale. However, they cannot top up their energy supplies for there are insufficient concentrations of food at their winter breeding sites to make it worthwhile to feed, so they fast.

Sleeping

Whales, like most animals, need to rest. Often as not they take a catnap at midday, and as soon as one whale sleeps, others follow suit. With just their back and dorsal fin showing, and their head and rostrum just below the surface, they resemble logs. When it is time to breathe, an automatic reflex brings up their head. Delicate receptors around the blowhole detect when the nostrils are above the surface, which causes them to open and the whale to take a breath. As soon as one whale in a sleeping group wakes up, the rest follow suit, and one by one they sound. When active, whales exhale when they surface and inhale when they sound, the opposite of seals and seal lions.

North Pacific breeding sites

When the Alaska whales head south, many go to Hawaii, but not all. In the western Pacific, for example, humpbacks congregate in waters close to Japan's Ryukyu (Nansei) Islands on the edge of the East China Sea and the Bonin (Ogasawara) Islands due south of Tokyo in winter.

In the eastern Pacific, there are humpbacks that feed predominantly in waters off Washington and California in summer, and head for Mexico in the winter. There are several traditional over-wintering grounds: the Revillagigedo Archipelago, a group of four volcanic islands about 240 miles (386km) southwest of the tip of Baja California; the northern Gulf of California; southern Baja California; and the mainland coast of Mexico, including the Islas Marías and Isla Isabel. There is also a sub-population that feeds predominantly off southern California in summer, but goes to Central America for the winter (see 'Migration north' above).

Some of the Mexican whales, though, can end up in any of five different summer locations – Oregon, California, Washington, British Columbia and Alaska. Their annual northward migration runs parallel to the Pacific coast of North America. However, they travel at a distance of anything between 30 and 600 miles (50 and 1,000km) offshore, so few of these animals are photographed en route. Many are absent from photo-ID data. And what is more, on reaching their summer sites, they feed many miles out in the ocean so shore-based observers would also not pick them out.

In a satellite tracking study by the Oregon researchers, one whale went from Mexico's Socorro Island to Vancouver Island, off the Canadian coast, staying close to the west coast of North America all the way. Another travelled well out to sea over 6,000 miles (10,000km) from Socorro to Alaska, its feeding sites overlapping with those of Hawaii's humpbacks.

There is also evidence from photo-identification studies that some whales are not loyal to a particular site but might well disperse to any of the traditional areas in the North Pacific. In winter, for example, male whales from southeast Alaska have been spotted in Baja California or Japan one year and Hawaii the next. A whale from British Columbia was also spotted at Ogasawara in Japan. This means that there is a certain amount of interbreeding between stocks, reducing the probability of inbreeding.

Predators

Undoubtedly the most dangerous predators to humpback whales are killer whales, especially during the migration. They are immediately recognisable by their black-and-white colouration and high dorsal fin. Female fins are curved, while the bull has a straight, sword-like fin. They live in family groups, known as pods, consisting of a handful of females and offspring and a single large bull. Pods sometimes congregate together to form temporary herds or aggregations, up to 500 individuals in one case. Orca pods along the Pacific coast of North America are known as either 'resident' pods, which tend to occupy a distinct home range and eat mainly fish, or free-ranging 'transient' pods, which like meat. A few groups even specialise in running down whales. Whatever their taste, they are all extremely vocal. They have an extraordinary vocabulary of cries, squeals, buzzes and burps, each pod with its own dialect. Several resident pods have similar dialects, indicating they were once part of the same ancestral pod. They are said to be part of a 'clan'. Resident pods and transient pods, however, communicate in very different ways when hunting. Resident pods, which mainly chase fish such as salmon, call continuously while herding their prey before them. Transient pods are silent, and sneak up on their prey unheard and unseen.

Transients feed mainly on marine mammals, including whales. In southeast Alaska, they tend to poke around bays and other quiet spots looking for harbour seals and Steller's sea lions. Rarely are people attacked. The exception was an aborted attack in August 2005 in Helm Bay, near Ketchikan, Alaska, when a 12-year-old boy was bumped on the chest and shoulder. The youngster was swimming underwater when he twice heard a sound like a rifle shot. He stopped and stood in water about chest high, only to be confronted with a six-feet-high dorsal fin. He looked underwater and was face to face with a bull killer whale, estimated to be nearly 25ft (8m) long. The rest of the pod of six whales surrounded them. A family friend grabbed the boy and they made for the beach. The whales meanwhile swam back and forth along the shore. One whale turned on its side and slapped first its pectoral fin and then its tail on the water. The other whales followed suit, as if signalling to the people on the beach. It is thought they had as big a fright as the boy, and they were showing their unease. They more than likely expected a harbour seal splashing in the shallows, and were brought up short when they met head-on with a human.

Most killer whale attacks on humpbacks in the northern Pacific region appear to be off the southwest coast of North America. The tooth rake marks on whale flukes are more prevalent on whales migrating between California and Mexico. Most attacks, surprisingly, are on calves on the wintering grounds, which negates the previously held view that whales migrate to tropical water to avoid predation.

Other dangers coming to light in recent years, especially to young calves, are from false killer whales, pilot whales and tiger sharks. Some whales show white oval scars probably inflicted by lampreys, and small circular scars probably from cookie-cutter sharks. Most whales are inundated with parasites, from whale lice outside to tapeworms inside. Barnacles grow on their snouts, chins and in their throat pleats. And paralytic shellfish poisoning has been implicated in whale deaths in New England.

Humans, however, still constitute the biggest threat.

Human threats
Whales feed day and night, and in southeast Alaska cruise ships travel by night. The two are not compatible, and many whales are injured or even killed as a result. With whaling less common, the main threats to humpback whales are collisions with ships, generally vessels more than 263ft (80m) in length and

travelling faster than 16mph (26km/h), and entanglement, principally with fishing gear. An estimated 71 per cent of southeast Alaska's humpbacks have been entangled at least once around their tailstock, and studies from the northwest Atlantic suggest that 20 per cent of that population become entangled every year. Humpbacks are not the only victims. It has been estimated that worldwide, 308,000 whales, dolphins and porpoises die every year from entanglement in fishing gear.

Humpbacks and history

People knew of humpbacks long before they were described for science. One of the earliest references is in 326 BC, when the Greek mariner Nearchus encountered whales off the coast of what is now Pakistan. They were thought to have been humpbacks, for they are still abundant in this area of the Arabian Sea. In later years, the whales were encountered all over the world and sailors from different countries gave them different names. The British once called the humpback the bunch whale, on account of what they considered a *bunch*, meaning a 'swelling' or 'bump', rather than a dorsal fin that was on the back near the tail. The French know it as *la baleine à bosse*, meaning 'whale with a hump', and the Germans know it as *Buckelwal*, meaning 'hump whale'. (A list of common names is included in Appendix II.)

The Spanish were among the first to recognise humpback nursery sites. In his *La General y natural historia de las Indias* ('The Natural and General History of the Indies'), Spanish historian and writer Gonzalo Fernández de Oviedo y Valdés (1478–1557) drew attention to adult whales and whale calves breaching in waters off Panama's west coast.

The British were among the first commercial whalers to exploit humpback whales. Along with northern right whales, they were discovered in the Arctic. British whaling ships, setting out mainly from Scottish ports, employed Basque whalers to catch them. Basque whaling tradition goes back to the 12th century.

Their natural curiosity meant that the humpbacks approached boats, and were harpooned for their trouble. The blubber was rendered down to make grade one oil, and used in the manufacture of margarine and soft soap. The meat was processed to produce a meat extract, and thereafter animal feed. Oil from the liver was marketed as a food supplement. The baleen plates were made into stiffening rods for women's corsets.

Sanctuary

Today, humpback whales are protected worldwide. In Hawaii, the Humpback Whale National Marine Sanctuary was designated by Congress in 1992, when it was recognised as the most important breeding habitat in the world and the only area in the USA where these whales come to breed, nurse and to mate. The US National Oceanic and Atmospheric Administration (NOAA) works with the community to preserve the habitat and the whales, and today the humpback whale is the official marine mammal for the state of Hawaii.

Occasionally whales strand. Often as not they are sick animals, disorientated and weak, that come into shallow water and strand to avoid drowning; then they die. Nevertheless, there are many strandings for which the cause is unknown. In Hawaii, there is a stranding network that both attempts to help stranded whales to get back to sea and investigate why they stranded in the first place. There are mercifully few, about five strandings here a year.

International cooperation
In an attempt to coordinate information on where humpbacks

go in the North Pacific and why, scientists from the USA, Canada, Mexico, Russia and Japan have been collaborating in an ambitious trans-Pacific project, known as SPLASH. All the photo-ID material from many humpback researchers, for example, is being consolidated at the National Marine Mammal Laboratory in Seattle, where it is made available to all the researchers involved. Already, unexpected results are forthcoming, such as a humpback from British Columbia being photographed off Japan. They have also discovered in some populations that female whales involved in entanglements have fewer calves, and that one in five whales have raking scars, probably from the teeth of killer whales. They have also recognised that calf mortality is 14–18 per cent each year, and the North Pacific population is increasing in numbers by about 7 per cent annually.

Anecdotes

While the whales have much to fear from us, we have little to fear from the whales. Whales will check out divers but a humpback has attacked nobody deliberately, not even an aggressive bull during a competitive brawl. BBC producer Martha Holmes and underwater cameraman Peter Scoones once came close to a serious situation when working on *Blue Planet*. They were in the water filming humpbacks when, just in time, Holmes spotted a male charging straight towards them. The crew on the dive boat said they did the closest thing to walking on water! The whale was, in fact, heading straight towards a female behind the duo, but woe betide anyone who gets in the way of a love-torn bull humpback.

Underwater photographer Flip Nicklin tells of how a male humpback used its long pectoral fin to draw him right into it, and check him out for what seemed an eternity, but was in reality just a few minutes. Nicklin was unharmed. A woman on a whale-watching cruise in Hawaii, though, was not so lucky. A baby whale was practising breaching and each breach brought it closer to the cruise boat. The skipper was understandably concerned, but it was too late. The whale breached right onto the back of the boat. The woman's leg was broken, but everybody survived, including the whale. A similar event with a large eagle ray off the Florida coast, when a woman was killed by a ray that had leapt accidentally onto the deck of her craft, shows how dangerous these situations can be. These are wild animals and their everyday behaviour can be boisterous, even dangerous if you are in the wrong place at the wrong time…and humpback whales are mighty big!

Occasionally, there are lighter moments. Dan Salden, founder of the Hawaii Whale Research Foundation, recalls a time when he was observing a female with a calf and a primary escort. The three whales seemed to be resting near the boat, when the mother and escort suddenly swam away, each performing three chin slaps as they went. They both breached. Salden, meanwhile, looked around only to find that the mother had left the calf with him. When they were about 150 yards (150m) away, they returned for him and just hung around the boat. Salden's team had provided 'day care' for a humpback. It seemed as if the mother had trusted their presence.

APPENDIX I

Hawaii geology

The Hawaiian Islands, and therefore the whales, are here because of a hotspot below the Earth's surface, where the Pacific floor passes over a weakness in the Earth's crust. Here, molten lava spews out from deep down in the bowels of our planet, forming a string of islands hundreds of miles long. The islands and islets to the west and northwest of the chain slid slowly over the hotspot eons ago and are now some distance from the active centre. Starved of lava, the sea slowly grinds them down. Many are no more than a few feet above sea level, yet they are host to enormous seabird colonies. The island of Midway, to the far west, and French Frigate Shoals, 300 miles (480km) west of Honolulu, are nesting sites for Laysan and black-footed albatrosses among others. Islands even further to the northwest have already disappeared below the waves, forming a subterranean mountain chain, the Empress seamounts.

The most active area currently is centred on 'Big Island' and the neighbouring submarine volcano Loihi, the newest peak but one yet to push above the sea's surface. Hawaii's Big Island is dominated by Mauna Kea and Mauna Loa, two massive shield volcanoes, but activity is confined mainly to smaller craters on their sides. Kilauea, for example, may be no more than a wart on the flanks of the great Mauna Loa, yet it is one of the most active volcanoes in the world. Its plumbing feeds magma to the surface from chambers 40 miles below.

Kilauea is home to Pele, the volcano goddess, who, according the Hawaiian legend, lives in the crater named *Halema'uma'u*, meaning 'house of ferns'. It is said that a jilted suitor built a house of ferns over the gaping hole to keep Pele from materialising and creating havoc by causing increasingly violent eruptions. He failed. Since 1983, the mountain has been disgorging lava from the cinder-and-splatter cone Pu'u 'O'o, which flows down the volcano through lava tubes a distance of seven miles (11km) to Paluma pali on the coast. In 1996, rivers of lava engulfed the towns of Kalapana and Kaimu, and Kalapana's black sand beach was replaced by molten basalt.

As red hot fingers of incandescent rock at a temperature of over 2,000 degrees enter the water, they generate clouds of choking smog laced with droplets of deadly sulphuric and hydrochloric acid. As water enters the lava tubes, lava bubbles over 60 feet (18m) high burst on the surface, splattering the rocks with glowing gobs of molten rock. Below the waves, the lava cools and solidifies into pillows of smooth, dark rock, new land in the middle of the vast ocean.

Maui is relatively young, but her two peaks – West Maui Volcano and Haleakala – have already moved away from the hotspot, the former extinct, the latter the world's largest dormant volcano, but it could still blow at any time. It was in their shadow and in the lee of neighbouring Molokai that many whales congregate, a haven for giants.

APPENDIX II

Common names for the humpback whale
Aliamak (Aleut)
Alkhiamak (Aleut)
Allamak (Aleut)
Kaipokak (Aleut)
Keporkak (Aleut)
Khi-tkhukkh (Aleut)

hrboun dlouhoploutvý (Czech)
keporkak (Czech)
Keporkak dlouhoplautvý (Czech)
keporkak dlouhoploutvý (Czech)
plejtvák dlouhoploutvý (Czech)
plejtvák keporkak (Czech)
velryba keporkak (Czech)

Buckelhval (Danish)
Pukkelhval (Danish)
Stubhval (Danish)

Bultrug (Dutch)
Langarmvinwisch (Dutch)

184

Penvisch (Dutch)

Bunch (English)
Bunch whale (English)
Hump-back (English)
Humpback whale (English)
Humpbacked whale (English)
Hump whale (English)
Hunch backed whale (English)

Baleine à bosse (French)
Baleine à taquet (French)
Baleine á bosse (French)
Baleine á taquet (French)
Baleine tampon (French)
Jubarte (French)
Mégaptère (French)
Rorqual à bosse (French)
Rorqual du cap (French)
Rorqual noueux (French)

Buckelwal (German)
Knurrwal (German)
Pflockfisch (German)

Balenottera gobba (Italian)
Megattera (Italian)

Zatokuzira (Japanese)

Valzius (Latvian)

Knölhval (Norwegian)

Trold-hval (Norwegian)

Pletwal (Polish)

Baleia de bossas (Portuguese)

Dlinnorukii polosatik (Russian)
Gorbach (Russian)
Gorbatyi kit (Russian)
Veselyi kit (Russian)

Ballena jorobada (Spanish)
Gubarte (Spanish)
Jorobada (Spanish)
Rorcual jorobado (Spanish)
Yubarta (Spanish)

Hnufubakur (Swedish)
Knölval (Swedish)
Puckelval (Swedish)

Reproduced by kind permission of the uBio Project at www.ubio.org

APPENDIX III

Scientific names

abalone	Family: Haliotidae
Arctic tern	*Sterna paradisaea*
Atka mackerel	*Pleurogrammus monopterygius*
bald eagle	*Haliaeetus leucocephalus*
bandit angelfish	*Holocanthus arcuatus*
Barrow's goldeneye	*Bucephala islandica*
basket star	*Gorgonocephalus eucnemis*
bat ray	*Myliobatis californica*
bat star	*Patiria minata*
big-eyed thresher shark	*Alopias superciliosus*
black bear	*Ursus americanus*
black-footed albatross	*Phoebastria nigripes*
black oystercatcher	*Haematopus bachmani*
blackpoll warbler	*Dendroica striata*
black sea cucumber	*Holothuria atra*
blacktail deer	*Odocoileus hemionus*
black triggerfish	*Melichthys niger*
blue rockfish	*Sebastes mystinus*
blue shark	*Prionace glauca*
blue whale	*Baleanoptera musculus*
bottlenose dolphin	*Tursiops truncatus*

box crab	*Calappa* spp.
brain coral	*Diploria* spp.
Bristle-thighed curlew	*Numenius tahitiensis*
brittlestar	Class: Ophiuroidea
brown booby	*Sula leucogaster*
brown pelican	*Pelecanus occidentalis*
cabezon	*Scorpaenichthys marmoratus*
capelin	*Malottus villosus*
Cassin's auklet	*Ptychoramphus aleuticus*
cauliflower coral	*Pocillopora* spp.
cedar	*Cedrus* spp.
Christmas-tree worms	*Spirobranchus* spp.
cleaner wrasse	*Labroides dimidiatus*
colossal squid	*Mesonychoteuthis hamiltoni*
comb jelly	Phylum: Ctenophora
common raven	*Corvus corax*
convict tang	*Acanthurus triostegus*
cookie-cutter shark	*Isistius brasiliensis*
cormorant	*Phalacrocorax* spp.
Dall's porpoise	*Phocoenoides dalli*
damselfish	Family: Pomacentridae
dunlin	*Calidris alpina*
dwarf lanternshark	*Etmopterus perryi*
eagle ray	*Aetobatus narinari*
euchalon	*Thaleichthys pacificus*
false killer whale	*Pseudorca crassidens*
feather-duster worms	Family: Sabellidae
finger coral	*Porites* spp.
fin whale	*Balaenoptera physalus*
fireweed	*Epilobium angustifolium*
forget-me-not	*Myosotis alpestris*
flying fish	Family: Exocoetidae
garden eel	*Heteroconger cobra*

ghost crab	*Ocypode* spp.
giant kelp	*Macrocystis* spp. and *Nereocystis* spp.
giant squid	*Architeuthis* spp.
glaucus-winged gull	*Larus glaucescens*
goatfish	Family: Mullidae
great barracuda	*Sphyraena barracuda*
great white shark	*Carcharodon carcharias*
green moray eel	*Gymnothorax prasinus*
green turtle	*Chelonia mydas*
grey reef shark	*Carcharhinus amblyrhynchos*
grey (or gray) whale	*Eschrichtius robustus*
grizzly bear	*Ursus arctos horribilis*
grunt sculpin	*Rhamphocottus richardsonii*
guillemot	*Uria* spp.
hairy woodpecker	*Picoides villosus*
harlequin duck	*Histrionicus histrionicus*
Hawaiian monk seal	*Monachus shauinslandia*
Hawaiian petrel	*Pterodroma sandwichensis*
Hawaiian silversword	*Argyroxiphium sandwicense*
hawksbill turtle	*Eretmochelys imbricata*
hemlock	*Tsuga* spp.
hermit crab	Superfamily: Paguroidea
horned puffin	*Fratercula corniculata*
humpback whale	*Megaptera novaeangliae*
jaeger	*Stercorarius* spp.
kelp	Order: Laminerariales
kelp bass	*Paralabrax clathratus*
kelp crab	*Pugettia producta*
killer whale	*Orcinus orca*
Kittlitz's murrelet	*Brachyramphus brevirostris*
krill	Order: Euphausiacea
lanternfish	Family: Myctophidae
laughing gull	*Larus atricilla*

Laysan albatross	*Phoebastria immutabilis*
leopard shark	*Triakis semifasciata*
ling cod	*Ophiodon elongatus*
lion's mane jellyfish	*Cyanea capillata*
loggerhead turtle	*Caretta caretta*
long-tailed duck	*Clangula hyemalis*
lupine	*Lupinus* spp.
magnificent frigatebird	*Fregata magnificens*
mahi mahi	*Coryphaena hippurus*
manta ray	*Manta birostris*
marbled murrelet	*Brachyramphus marmoratus*
market squid	*Loligo opalescens*
marlin	*Tetrapturus* spp. and *Makaira* spp.
megamouth	*Megachasma pelagios*
mongoose	*Herpestes javanicus*
moon jellyfish	*Aurelia aurita*
moray eel	Family: Muraenidae
Moorish idol	*Zanclus cornutus*
murre	*Uria* spp.
nagoonberry	*Rubus arcticus*
neon flying squid	*Ommastrephes bartami*
northern elephant seal	*Mirounga angustirostris*
northern minke whale	*Baleanoptera acutorostrus*
northern waterthrush	*Seiurus noveboracensis*
North Pacific giant octopus	*Enteroctopus dofleini*
oceanic white-tip shark	*Carcharhinus longimanus*
ocean sunfish	*Mola mola*
orange cup coral	*Balanophyllia elegans*
Pacific angel shark	*Squatina californica*
Pacific bluefin tuna	*Thunnus orientalis*
Pacific bonito	*Sarda chiliensis*
Pacific chub mackerel	*Scomber japonicus*
Pacific cleaner shrimp	*Lysmata amboinensis*

Pacific Dover sole	*Microstomus pacificus*
Pacific fulmar	*Procellaria pacifica*
Pacific golden plover	*Pluvialis fulva*
Pacific hagfish	*Eptatretus stouti*
Pacific hake	*Merluccius productus*
Pacific halibut	*Hippoglossus stenolepsis*
Pacific harbour seal	*Phoca vitulina*
Pacific herring	*Clupea pallasii*
Pacific kittiwake	*Rissa tridactyla pollicaris*
Pacific rockfish	*Sebastes* spp.
Pacific sanddab	*Citharichthys sordidus*
Pacific sand lance	*Ammodytes hexapterus*
Pacific saury	*Cololabis saira*
Pacific sleeper shark	*Somniosus pacificus*
Pacific spotted dolphin	*Stenella attenuata*
Pacific torpedo ray	*Torpedo californica*
parrotfish	Family: Scaridae
peacock grouper	*Cephalopholis argus*
pelagic red crab	*Pleuroncodes planipes*
peregrine	*Falco peregrinus*
pillar coral	*Dendrogyra cylindricus*
pilot fish	*Naucrates ductor*
pink-footed shearwater	*Puffinus creatopus*
pipefish	Subfamily: Syngnathinae
pollack	*Pollachius* spp.
prickleback	Family: Stichaeidae
pufferfish	Family: Tetraodonidae
purple jellyfish	*Pelagia noctiluca*
raccoon	*Procyon lotor*
ratfish	Order: Chimaeriformes
razorbill	*Alca torda*
red cedar	*Thuja plicata*
red fox	*Vulpes vulpes*

red turban shell	*Astrea gibberose*
remora	Family: Echeneidae
rock gunnel	*Pholis gunnellus*
rock sandpiper	*Calidris ptilocnemis*
sablefish	*Anoplopoma fimbria*
sailfish	*Istiophorus platypterus*
salmon	Family: Salmonidae
salp	Family: Salpidae
sand eel	Family: Ammodytidae
sanderling	*Calidris alba*
sandhill crane	Grus canadensis
sculpin	Superfamily: Cottoidea
sea anemone	Order: Actiniaria
sea fan	Order: Gorgonacea
sea lily	Class: Crinoidea
sea otter	*Enhydra lutris*
sea plume	Order: Gorgonacea
sea whip	Order: Gorgonacea
sei whale	*Balaenoptera borealis*
senorita wrasse	*Oxyjulis californica*
shag	*Phalacrocorax* spp.
sharp-shinned hawk	*Accipeter striata*
shiner perch	*Cymatogaster aggregata*
short-finned pilot whale	*Globicephala melaena*
silky shark	*Carcharhinus falciformis*
silverweed	*Argentina anserina*
skeleton shrimp	Supraorder: Caprellida
skipjack	*Katsuwonus pelamis*
snailfish	Family: Liparidae
soldierfish	Subfamily: Myripristinae
sooty shearwater	*Puffinus griseus*
southern minke whale	*Balaenoptera bonaerensis*
speckled sea cucumber	*Actinopyga mauritiana*

sperm whale	*Physeter macrocephalus*
spike prawns	*Saron marmoratus*
spinner dolphin	*Stenella longirostris*
spiny lobster	*Panulirus* spp.
spruce	*Picea* spp.
squat lobster	Family: Galatheidae
squirrelfish	Subfamily: Holocentrinae
Steller's sea lion	*Eumetopias jubatus*
storm petrel	Family: Hydrobatidae
surfbird	*Aphriza virgata*
Swainson's hawk	*Buteo swainsoni*
swordfish	*Xiphias gladius*
tiger shark	*Galeocerdo cuvier*
tree sparrow	*Spizella arborea*
triggerfish	Family: Balistidae
trumpetfish	*Aulostomus maculatus*
umbrella octopus	*Grimpoteuthis tuftsi*
vase sponge	*Callyspongia* spp.
vermillion rockfish	*Sebastes miniatus*
vole	*Microtus* spp.
wahoo	*Acanthocybium solandri*
walleye pollack	*Theregra chalcogramma*
western gull	*Larus occidentalis*
western sandpiper	*Calidris mauri*
white-tailed tropicbird	*Phaethon lepturus*
white-tip reef shark	*Triaenodon obesus*
wolf eel	*Anarthys ocellatus*
wrasse	Family: Labridae
yellowfin tuna	*Thunnus albacares*
yellowtail	*Seriola* spp.
yellow-rumped warbler	*Dendroica coronata*
jjpae'ula	*Halocardina rubra*
zombie worm	*Osedax* spp.

APPENDIX IV

Resources: Useful websites

Alaska Fish and Wildlife News
   http://www.wildlifenews.alaska.gov
Alaska Sea Grant
   http://seagrant.uaf.edu/news
Alaska Whale Foundation
   http://www.alaskawhalefoundation.org
American Cetacean Society
   http://www.acsonline.org
British Columbia Ferries
   http://www.bcferries.com/schedules/inside/
British Columbia Parks
   http://www.env.gov.bc.ca/bcparks
British Divers Marine Life Rescue
   http://www.bdmlr.org.uk
The Centre for Cetacean Research and Conservation
   http://www.whaleresearch.org
Centre for Oceanic Research and Education
   http://www.coreresearch.org
The Centre for Whale Research (Western Australia)
   http://www.cwr.org.au
The Centre for Whale Studies
   http://www.centerforwhalestudies.org

Cetacean Society International
  http://csiwhalesalive.org
Cetos Research Organisation
  http://www.cetosresearch.org
The Dolphin Institute
  http://www.dolphin-institute.org
European Cetacean Society
  http://www.broekemaweb.nl/ecs
Farallon Island Waste Dump
  http://walrus.wr.usgs.gov/farallon/radwaste
Florida Museum of Natural History
  http://www.flmnh.ufl.edu/fish/sharks
Hawaiian Islands Humpback Whale
Marine Sanctuary
  http://Hawaiihumpbackwhale.noaa.gov
Hawaii Volcano Observatory
  http://hvo.wr.usgs.gov
Hawaii Whale Research Foundation
  http://www.hwrf.org
Hebridean Whale and Dolphin Trust
  http://www.whaledolphintrust.co.uk
International Whaling Commission
  http://www.iwcoffice.org
Intersea Foundation
  http://www.intersea.org
The Irish Whale and Dolphin Group
  http://www.iwdg.ie
Marine Mammal Centre (California)
  http://www.marinemammalcenter.org
Marine Mammal Institute (Oregon University)
  http://mmi.oregonstate.edu
The Maui News
  http://www.mauinews.com

Monterey Bay Whale Watch
 http://www.gowhales.com
National University of Singapore
 http://www.arl.nus.edu.sg/web/research/whale
National Wildlife
 http://www.nationalwildlife.org/nationalwildlife
NOAA Ocean Explorer
 http://www.oceanexplorer.noaa.gov
NOAA Undersea Research Programme
 http://www.nurp.noaa.gov/Spotlight/Whales
Ocean Alliance
 http://www.oceanalliance.org
The Oceania Project
 http://www.oceania.org.au
Ocean Mammal Institute
 http://www.oceanmammalinst.org
Opération Cétacés: New Caledonia
 http://www.operationcetaces.com
Pacific Wildlife Foundation and
West Coast Whale Research Foundation
 http://www.pwlf.org
Provincetown Centre for Coastal Studies
 http://www.coastalstudies.org
Sea Watch Foundation
 http://www.seawatchfoundation.org.uk
Western Whale Research
 http://www.whaleswa.com.au
The Whale and Dolphin Conservation Society
 http://www.wdcs.org
The Whale and Dolphin Conservation Society – Australasia
 http://www.wdcs.org.au
Whale Centre of New England
 http://www.whalecenter.org

Whalepower (blade technology)
   http://www.whalepower.com/drupal
Whales Alive
   http://www.whalesalive.org.au
Whale Trust
   http://www.whaletrust.org

REFERENCES

Anon (2004). Golden Gate Transits' Humphrey the Whale Bus Announces its Retirement on eBay. Golden Gate Bridge Highway and Transportation District, retrieved 19 May 2008 at: http://goldengate.org/b/news/WhaleBusSale.php

Anon (2007). Bird Gallery of the Hawaii Audubon Society, retrieved 28 September from http://www.hawaiiaudubon.com

Arnold, Josh (1999). Ten Years and Still Spewin: OPA 90 and the legacy of the Exxon Valdez, in *Letter of the Law*, last sourced on 9 April 2008 at: http://www.lclark.edu/~lotl/volume5issue5/

Au, W.W., Mobley, L.J., Burgess, W.C., Lammers, M.O. and Nachtigall, P.E. (2000). Seasonal and diurnal trends of chorusing humpback whales wintering in waters off western Maui. *Marine Mammal Science*, 16: 530–544.

Baird, R.W., D.J. McSweeney, C.Bane, J. Barlow, D.R. Salden, L.K. Antoine, R.G. LeDuc, and D.L. Webster (2006). Killer Whales in Hawaiian Waters: Information on Population Identity and Feeding Habits. *Pacific Science*, vol: 60, no: 4, 523–530.

Baker, C.S., and Herman, L.M. (1981). Migration and local movements of humpback whales through Hawaiian waters. *Canadian Journal of Zoology* 59, 530–544.

Baker, C.S., and Herman, L.M. (1984). Aggressive behaviour between humpback whales wintering in Hawaiian waters. *Canadian Journal of Zoology* 62, 1922–1937.

Baker, C.S. and Herman, L.M. (1985). Whales that go to extremes. *Natural History*, October 1985, 52–60.

Baker, C.S., Herman, L.M., Perry, A., Lawton, W.S., Straley, J.M., and

Straley, J.H. (1985). Population characteristics and migration of summer and later season humpback whales in southeastern Alaska. *Marine Mammal Science* 1, 304–323.

Baker, C.S., Perry, A., and Herman, L.M. (1987). Reproductive histories of female humpback whales in the North Pacific. *Marine Ecology Progress Series* 41, 103–114.

Balridge, A. (1972). Killer Whales Attack and Eat a Grey Whale. *Journal of Mammology*, vol: 53, no: 4, 898–900.

Baraff, L. and Weinrich, M.T. (1993). Separation of humpback whale mothers and calves on a feeding ground in early Autumn. *Marine Mammal Science* 9, 431–434.

Barlow, J. and Clapham, P.J. (1997). A new birth-interval approach to estimating demographic parameters of humpback whales. *Ecology* 78, 535–546.

Block, B.A., Weng, Kevin C. (2004). Diel vertical migration of the big eye thresher (*Alopias superciliosus*), a species possessing orbital retia mirabilia. *Fishery Bulletin*, National Marine Fisheries Service.

Bosley, K.A., J.W. Lavelle, R.D. Brodeur, W.W. Wakefield, R.L. Emmett, E.T. Baker, and K.M. Rehmke (2004). Biological and physical processes in and around Astoria submarine Canyon, Oregon, USA. *Journal of Marine Systems*, 50: 21– 37.

Brown, M.R. and Corkeron, P.J. (1995). Pod characteristics of migrating humpback whales off the East Australian Coast. *Behaviour* 132, 163–179.

Brown, M.R., Corkeron, P.J., Hale, P.T., Schultz, K.W., and Bryden, M.M. (1995). Evidence for a sex segregated migration in the humpback whale. *Proceedings of the Royal Society of London, Series B: Biological Sciences* 259, 229–234.

Calambokidis J., Steiger G.H, Rasmussen K., Urbán-R J and others (2000) Migratory destinations of humpback whales from the California, Oregon and Washington feeding ground. *Marine Ecology Progress Series* 192:295–304

Calambokidis, J., Steiger, G.H., Straley, J.M., Quinn, T., Barlow, J., Herman, L.M., Cerchio, S., Salden, D.R., Yamaguchi, M., Sato, F., Urban, J., Jacobsen, R.J., von Ziegesar, O., Balcomb, K.C., Gabriele, C.M., Dahlheim, M.E., Higashi, N., Ford, J.K.B., Miyura, Y., Ladron de Guevara, P., Mizroch, S.A., Schlender, L., and Rasmussen, K. (1997). Population, abundance, and structure of humpback whales in the North Pacific Basin. Draft final report to

Southwest Fisheries Science Center, La Jolla, CA by Cascadia Research Collective, 218 1/2 West Fourth Avenue, Olympia, WA.

Cerchio S. (1998). Estimates of humpback whale abundance off Kauai,1989–1993: evaluating biases associated with sampling the Hawaiian Islands breeding assemblage. *Marine Ecology Progress Series* 175:23–34.

Chaloupka, M. and Osmond, M. (1999). Spatial and seasonal distribution of humpback whales in the Great Barrier Reef Region. *American Fisheries Society Symposium* 23, 89–106.

Charif, R.A., P.J. Clapham, C.W. Clark (2001). Acoustic Detections Of Singing Humpback Whales in Deep Waters off the British Isles. *Marine Mammal Science* 17 (4) , 751–768.

Chittleborough, R.G. (1954). Studies on the ovaries of the humpback whale on the western Australian coast. *Australian Journal of Marine and Freshwater Research* 5, 35–63.

Chittleborough, R.G. (1955). Aspects of reproduction in the male humpback whale. *Australian Journal of Marine and Freshwater Research* 6, 1–29.

Chittleborough, R.G. (1958). The breeding cycle of the female humpback whale. *Australian Journal of Marine and Freshwater Research* 9, 1–18.

Chittleborough, R.G. (1959). Determination of age in the humpback whale. *Australian Journal of Marine and Freshwater Research* 10, 125–143.

Chittleborough, R.G. (1965). Dynamics of two populations of the humpback whale. *Australian Journal of Marine and Freshwater Research* 16, 33–128.

Chu, N.C. and Harcourt, P. (1986). Behavioural correlations with aberrant patterns in humpback whale songs. *Behavioural Ecology and Sociobiology* 19:309–312.

Clapham, P.J. (1992). Age at attainment of sexual maturity in humpback whales. *Canadian Journal of Zoology* 70:1470–1472.

Clapham, P.J. (1996). The social and reproductive biology of humpback whales: an ecological perspective. *Mammal Review* 26, 27–49.

Clapham, P.J., and Mattila, D.K. (1990). Humpback whale songs as indicators of migrations routes. *Marine Mammal Science* 6, 155–160.

Clapham, P. J., and Mayo, C. A. (1987). Reproduction and recruitment of individually identified humpback whales observed in Massachusetts Bay, 1979–1985. *Canadian Journal of Zoology* 65, 2853–2863.

Clapham, P.J., and Mayo, C.A. (1990). Reproduction of humpback whales observed in the Gulf of Maine. *Report of the International Whaling Commission (Special Issue 12)*, 171–175.

Clapham, P.J. and Mead, J.G. (1999). *Megaptera novaeangliae. Mammalian Species* 604, 1–9.

Clapham, P.J. and Palsboll, P.J. (1997). Molecular analysis of paternity shows promiscuous mating in female humpback whales. *Proceedings of the Royal Society of London, Series B: Biology* 264, 95–98.

Clapham, P.J., Palsboll, P.J., Mattila, D.K., and Vasquez, O. (1992). Composition and dynamics of humpback whales competitive groups in the West Indies. *Behaviour* 122, 182–194.

Clark, C.W. and Clapham, P.J. (2004). Acoustic monitoring on a humpback whale (*Megaptera novaeangliae*) feeding ground shows continual singing into late spring. *Proceedings of the Royal Society of London*, 271: 1051–1057.

Clutton-Brock, T.H. (1989). Mammalian mating systems. *Proceedings of the Royal Society of London.* 236: 339–372.

Clutton-Brock, T.H., Guiness, F.E., and Albon, S.D. (1982). Red deer – behavior and ecology of two sexes. *Wildlife behavior and ecology series.* University of Chicago Press, Chicago, IL.

Corkeron, P.J., and R.C. Connor (1999). Why do baleen whales migrate? *Marine Science* 15, 1228–1245.

Craig, A.S., and L.M. Herman (1997). Sex differences in site fidelity and migration of humpback whales to the Hawaiian Islands. *Canadian Journal of Zoology* 75, 1923–1933.

Craig, A.S. and L.M. Herman (2000). Habitat preferences of female humpback whales in the Hawaiian Islands are associated with reproductive status. Marine Ecology Progress Series, 193, 209–216.

Croll, D.A., C.W. Clark, A. Acevedo, B. Tershy, S. Flores, J. Gedamke, and J. Urban (2002). Only male fin whales sing loud songs. *Nature* vol: 417, p.809.

Darling, J.D., Gibson, K.M., & Silber, G.K. (1983). Observations on the abundance and behaviour of humpback whales off West Maui, Hawaii, 1977–79. In R.S. Payne (Ed.), *Communication and Behaviour of whales* (pp. 201–222). Boulder, CO: Westview Press.

Darling, J.D. and Berube, M. (2001). Interactions of singing humpback whales with other males. *Marine Mammal Science*, 17: 570–584.

Darling, J.D., M.E. Jones and C.P. Nicklin (2006). Humpback whale songs: Do they organize males during the breeding season? *Behaviour* 143, 1051–1101

Darling, J.D. (2001). Characterization of behavior of humpback whales in Hawaiian waters. Video and photographs by Charles "Flip" Nicklin. Summary last sourced on 27 April 2008 at: www.hawaiihumpbackwhale.noaa.gov/research/HIHWNMS_Research_Biblio.pdf

Dawbin, W.H. (1966). The seasonal migratory cycle of humpback whales. In K.S. Norris (Ed.), *Whales, dolphins, and porpoises* (pp.145–170). Berkley, CA: University of California Press.

Dawbin, W.H. (1997). Temporal segregation of humpback whales during migrations in Southern Hemisphere waters. *Memoirs of the Queensland Museum* 42, 105–138.

Dohl, T.P. (1983). Return of the humpback whale to central California. *Proceedings 5th Biennial Conference on the Biology of Marine Mammals*, Boston, MA. Abstracts, p.23.

Dolphin, W.F. (1985). Moods and Manners of Humpback Whales. *Animal Kingdom*, February/March, pp.40–45

D'Vincent, C.G., Nilson, R.M., and Hanna, R.E. (1985). Vocalization and coordinated feeding behaviour of the humpback whale in southeastern Alaska. *Scientific Reports of the Whales Research Institute* No. 36:11–47.

D'Vincent, C.G., Nilson, R.M., and Sharpe, F.A. (1988). Observations of humpback whale mother–calf pairs in Southeast Alaska. *Cetus* 8: 25–26.

D'Vincent, Cynthia, with Delphine Haley and Fred A. Sharpe (1989). *Voyaging with Whales*, Oakwell Boulton (Toronto).

Ford, J.K., Ellis, G.M., Matkin, D.R., Balcomb, K.C. Briggs, D., Morton, A.B. (2005). Killer Whale Attacks on Minke Whales: Prey Capture and Antipredator Tactics. *Marine Mammal Science* 21:4, 603–618

Ford, J.K. and Reeves, R.R. (2008). Fight or flight: antipredator strategies of baleen whales. *Mammal Review* 38:1, 50–86

Forestell, P.H. and Kaufman, G.D. (1990). The history of whale watching in Hawaii and its role in enhancing visitor appreciation for endangered species. *Congress on Coastal and Marine Tourism* (pp.399–407). Honolulu, Hawaii, May 25–31.

Frank, T.M. and Widder, E.A. (1996). UL light in the deep-sea: In situ measurements of downwelling irradiance in relation to the visual threshold sensitivity of UV-sensitive crustaceans. *Mar. Fresh. Behav. Physiol.* 27(2-3): 189–197.

Frankel, A.S., Clark, C.W., Herman, L.M. and Gabriele, C.M. (1995). Spatial distribution, habitat utilization and social interactions of humpback whales off Hawaii, determined using acoustic and visual techniques. *Canadian Journal of Zoology* 73, 1134–1146.

Frantzis, A., Nicholaou, O. Bompar, J.-M., and Cammedda, A. (2004). Humpback whale occurrence in the Mediterranean Sea. *Journal of Cetacean Research and Management*, 6 (1): 25–28.

Fuller, M., Goree, W.S., and Goodman, W.L. (1985). An introduction to the use of SQUID magnetometers in biomagnetism. In *Magnetite Biomineralization and Magnetoreception in Organisms: A New Biomagnetism* (ed. J.L. Kirschvink, D.S. Jones and B.J. MacFadden) pp.103–151. New York: Plenum Press.

Gabriele, C.M., Straley, J.M., Herman, L.M., and Coleman, R.J. (1996). Fastest documented migration of a North Pacific humpback whale. *Marine Mammal Science*, 12: 457–464.

Gaskin, D.E. (1982). *The Ecology of Whales and Dolphins*. Heinemann Educational Books Ltd.

Gaydos, J.K., Raferty, S., Baird, R.W., and Osborne, R.W. (2005). Suspected Surplus Killing of Harbour Seal Pups by Killer Whales. *Northwestern Naturalist* 86:150–154.

Glockner, D.A. (1983). Determining the sex of humpback whales in their natural environment. In R.S. Payne (Ed.), *Communication and Behaviour of Whales* (pp.447–464). Boulder, CO: Westview Press.

Glockner-Ferrari, D.A. and Ferrari, M.J. (1984). Reproduction in humpback whale in Hawaiian waters. *Reports of the International Whaling Commission* (Special Issue 6), 237–242.

Glockner-Ferrari, D.A. and Ferrari, M.J. (1985). *Individual identification, behaviour, reproduction, and distribution of humpback whales in Hawaii*. Marine Mammal Commission, Washington, D.C., Report to MMC-83/06.

Glockner-Ferrari, D.A. and Ferrari, M.J. (1990). Reproduction in the humpback whale in Hawaiian waters, 1975–1988: the life history, reproductive rates and behaviour of known individuals identified through surface and underwater photography. *Reports of the International Whaling Commission* (Special Issue 12), 161–169.

Greenough, J.W. (1981). Whales at Table. *Natural History*, December 1981, pp.30–35

Hain, J.H.W., Carter, G.R., Kraus, S.D., Mayo, C.A., and Evans, H.E. (1982). Feeding behaviour of the humpback whale in the western North Atlantic. *Fisheries Bulletin* 80, 259–268.

203

Hall, H., and M. Hall (1981). Night of the Squid, last sourced on 18 April 2008 at: http://www.howardhall.com/stories/market_squid.html

Hayes, H.E., Winn, H.E., and Petricig, R. (1985). Anomalous feeding behaviour of a humpback whale. *Journal of Mammalogy*, 66 (4): 819–821.

Helweg, D.A., Herman, L.M., Yamamoto, S., and Forestell, P. (1990). Comparison of songs of humpback whales recorded in Japan, Hawaii and Mexico during the winter of 1989. *Scientific Records of Cetacean Research*, 1–20.

Helweg, D.A. and Herman, L.M. (1994). Diurnal patterns of behaviour and group membership of humpback whales wintering in Hawaiian waters. *Ethology* 98, 298–311.

Herman, L.M. (1979). Humpback whales in Hawaiian waters: A study in historical ecology. *Pacific Science* 33: 1–15.

Herman, L.M. and Antinoja, R.C. (1977). Humpback whales in the Hawaiian breeding waters: population and pod characteristics. *Scientific Reports of the Whales Research Institute* 29: 59–85.

Herman, L.M., Forestell, P.H., and Antinoja, R.C. (1980). *The 1976/77 migration of humpback whales into Hawaiian waters: Composite description.* Marine Mammal Commission, Washington, D.C., Report MMC–77/19.

Herman, L.M. and Tavolga, W.N. (1980). The communication system of cetaceans. In L.M. Herman (Ed.), *Cetacean behaviour: Mechanisms and Functions* (pp. 149–209). New York: Wiley Interscience.

Ingebrigsten, A. (1929). Whales caught in the North Atlantic and other seas. *Rapports et Procès-Verbaux des Reunion Conseil International pour L'Exploration de la Mer* 56 (2): 1–26.

Johnson, O.W., Warnock, N., Bishop, M.A., Bennett, A.J., Johnson, P.M., and Keinholtz, R.J. (1997). Migration by radio-tagged Pacific golden plovers from Hawaii to Alaska, and their subsequent survival. *The Auk*, 114 (3): 521–524.

Jurasz, C.M. and Jurasz, V.P. (1979). Feeding modes of the humpback whale in Southeast Alaska. *Scientific Reports of the Whales Research Institute* 31: 69–83.

Katona, S., Baxter, B., Brazier, O., Kraus, S., Perkins J., and Whitehead, H. (1979). Identification of humpback whales by fluke photographs. *Behaviour of marine animals*, Vol. 3 (Winn, H.E. & Olla, B.L., eds). Plenum Press, New York, pp.33–44.

Kaulukukui Jr, T. (2007). *History of Hawaii and Hawaiians.* Speech delivered at National Museum of American Indian, Washington D.C., retrieved on 28 September 2007 from: http://www.ksbe.edu/article.php?story=20070502150618378

Kirschvink, J.L. and Gould, J.L. (1981). Biogenic magnetite as a basis for magnetic field detection. *Biosystems* 13: 181–201.

Kunzig, Robert (1997) At home with jellies: observations on these sea creatures. *Discover*, September 1, 1997 (Gale Group, Michigan).

Laist, D.W., Knowlton, A.R., Mead, J.G., Collet, A.S. and M. Podesta (2001). Collisions Between Ships and Whales. *Marine Mammal Science*, 17 (1): 35–75.

Lambertsen, R.H., Baker, C.S., Duffield, D.A., and Chamberlin-Lea, J. (1988). Cytogenic determination of gender among individually identified humpback whales. *Canadian Journal of Zoology*, 66: 1243–1248.

Mackintosh, N.A. (1972). Biology of the populations of large whales. *Science Progress (Oxford)* 60: 449–464.

McDonald, M.A., Hildebrand, J.A., and Webb, S.C. (1995). Blue and fin whales observed on a seafloor array in the Northeast Pacific. *Journal of the Acoustic Society of America*. 98 (2).

McSweeney, D.J., Chu, K.C., Dolphin, W.F., and Guinee, L.N. (1989). North Pacific humpback whale songs: A comparison of southeast Alaskan feeding ground songs and Hawaiian wintering ground songs. *Marine Mammal Science* 5: 116–138.

Manuel, C., Jann, B., Seton, R., and Wenzel, F. (1999). Present Status of Humpback Whales in the Cape Verde Islands. 13th Biennial Conference on the Biology of Marine Mammals, Maui, Hawaii.

Mate, B.R., Gisiner, R., and Mobley, J. (1998). Local and migratory movements of Hawaiian humpback whales tracked by satellite telemetry. *Canadian Journal of Zoology*. 76: 863–868.

Mate, B.R., Mesecar, R., and Lagerquist, B. (2007). The evolution of satellite-monitored radio tags for large whales: One laboratory's experience. *Deep-Sea Research II*. 54: 224–247.

Matthews, L.H. (1937). The humpback whale. *Discovery Reports* 17, 7–92.

Mattila, D.K. and Clapham, P.J. (1989). Humpback whales and other cetaceans on Virgin Bank and in the northern Leeward Islands, 1985 and 1986. *Canadian Journal of Zoology* 67: 2201–2211.

Mattila, D.K., Clapham, P.J., Vasquez, O., and Bowman, R.S. (1994). Occurrence, population composition, and habitat use of humpback whales in Samana Bay, Dominican Republic. *Canadian Journal of Zoology*, 72: 1898–1907.

Mattila, D.K., Guinee, L.N., and Mayo, C.A. (1987). Humpback whale songs on a North Atlantic feeding ground. *Journal of Mammalogy* 68: 880–883.

Medrano, L., Salas, I., Ladron de Guevara, P., Salinas, M., Aguayo, A., Jacobsen, J., and Baker, C.S. (1994). Sex identification of humpback whales on the wintering grounds of Mexican Pacific. *Canadian Journal of Zoology*, 72: 1771–1774.

Mobley, J.R. Jr., Bauer, G.B., and Herman, L.M. (1999). Changes over a ten-year interval in the distribution and relative abundance of humpback whales wintering in Hawaiian waters. *Aquatic Mammals*, 25: 63–72.

Mobley, J.R. Jr., Forestell, P.H., and Grotefendt, R.A. (1997). Preliminary results of 1993 and 1995 aerial surveys of Hawaiian waters. In P.M. Payne, B. Phillips & E.T. Nitta (Eds.), *Reports of the workshop to assess research and other needs and opportunities related to humpback whales management in the Hawaiian Islands* (pp.1–8). U.S. Department of Cmmerce, NOAA Technical Memorandum NMFS-OPR-11.

Mobley, J.R. Jr., and Herman, L.M. (1985). Transience of social affiliations among humpback whales in the Hawaiian wintering grounds. *Canadian Journal of Zoology*, 63: 762–772.

Naessig, P.J. and J.M. Lanyon (2004). Levels and probable origin of predatory scarring on humpback whales in east Australian waters. *Wildlife Research* 31(2): 163–170.

Nagasawa, K., and Matani, Y. (2004). A humpback whale from the Pleistocene Kioroshi Formation of Imba-mura, Chiba Prefecture, central Japan. *Paleontological Research*, 8 (3):155–165.

Nasu, K. (1963). Oceanography and the whaling grounds in the subarctic regions of the Pacific Ocean. *Scientific Reports of the Whales Research Institute* 17, 105–156.

Neilson, J.L., Gabriele, C.M., and Straley, J.M. (2007). Humpback Whale Entanglement in Fishing Gear in Northern Southeastern Alaska, *Proceedings of the Fourth Glacier Bay Science Symposium*, pp.204–207.

Nemoto, T. (1957). Foods of the baleen whales in the northern Pacific. *Scientific Reports to the Whales Research Institute*, 12: 33–90.

Nemoto, T. (1959). Food of the baleen whales with reference to whales' movements. *Scientific Reports to the Whales Research Institute*, 14: 149–290.

Nishiwaki, M. (1959). Humpback whales in Ryukyuan waters. *Scientific Reports of the Whales Research Institute*, 14: 49–87.

Nishiwaki, M. (1966). Distribution and migration of the larger cetaceans in the North Pacific as shown by Japanese whaling results. In K.S. Norris (Ed.), *Whales, dolphins, and porpoises* (pp.171–191). Berkeley, CA: University of California Press.

NOAA. (1997). *Final environmental impact statement and management plan for the Hawaiian Islands Humpback Whale National Marine Sanctuary.* Silver Spring, MD: U.S. Department of Commerce.

Omura, H. (1955). Whales in the northern part of the North Pacific. *Norsk Hvalfangst-Tidende,* 44: 323–345.

Pack, A.A., Salden, D.R., Ferrari, M.J., Glockner-Ferrari, D.A., Herman, L.M., Stubbs H.A., and Straley, J.M. (1998). Male humpback whale dies in competitive group, *Marine Mammal Science,* 14: 861–873.

Payne, K.P. and Payne, R.S. (1985). Large scale changes over 19 years in songs of humpback whales of Bermuda. *Zeitschrift fur Tierpsychologie,* 68: 89–114.

Payne, K.P., Tyack, P. and Payne, R. (1983). Progressive changes in the songs of humpback whales (*Megaptera novaeangliae*): A detailed analysis of two seasons in Hawaii. *Communication and behaviour in whales* (Payne, R., ed.). Westview Press, Boulder, Colorado, pp.9–57.

Payne, R.S., and McVay, S. (1971). Songs of humpback whales. *Science* 173, 585–597.

Perry, A., C.S. Baker, and L.M. Herman (1990). Population characteristics of individually identified humpback whales in the central and eastern North Pacific: a summary and critique. In G.P. Donovan (ed) *Reports of the International Whaling Commission* (Special Issue 12: Photo-Identification) pp. 307–317.

Pike, G.C. and MacAskie, I.B. (1969). Marine mammals of British Columbia. *Bulletin of the Fisheries Research Board of Canada,* 171: 1–54.

Pitman, R.L. and S.J. Chivers (1998) Terror in Black and White – killer whales attacking sperm whales. *Natural History,* December 1998.

Pitman, R.L., Balance, L.T., Mesnick, S.I., and Chivers, S.J. (2001). Killer whale predation on sperm whales: observations and implications. *Marine Mammal Science,* 17 (3): 494–507.

Pivorunas, A. (1979). The feeding mechanisms of baleen whales. *American Scientist,* 67: 432–440.

Rasmussen, K., D.M. Palacios, J. Calambokidis, M.T. Saborío, L.D. Rosa, E.R. Secchi, G.H. Steiger, J.M. Allen and G.S. Stone (2007). Southern Hemisphere humpback whales wintering off Central America: insights from water temperature into the longest mammalian migration. *Biology Letters,* 3 (3): 302–305.

Rasmussen, K., J.Calambokidis and G.H. Steiger (2002). Humpback Whales and Other Marine Mammals Off Costa Rica and Surrounding Waters, 1996–2002, last sourced on 9 April 2008 at: www.cascadiaresearch.org/reports/rep-cr02.pdf

Razafindrakoto, Y., Rosenbaum, H.C., Helwweg, D.A. (2001). First description of humpback whale song from Antongil Bay, Madagascar. *Marine Mammal Science*, 17 (1): 180.

Reidenberg, J.S. and Laitman, J.T. (2007). Blowing bubbles: an aquatic adaptation that risks protection of the respiratory tract in humpback whales. *Anatomical Record (Hoboken)* 290 (6): 569–80

Rhodes, D.L. (2001). A Cultural History of Three Hawaiian Sites on the West Coast of Hawaii Island last sources on 9 April 2008 at: http://www.nps.gov/history/history/online_books/kona/history5e.htm

Rice, D.W. (1978). The humpback whale in the North Pacific: Distribution, exploitation, and numbers. In K.S. Norris and R. Reeves (Eds.), *Report on a workshop on problems related to humpback whales in Hawaii,* Report to the U.S. Marine Mammal Commission, Washington, D.C., pp.29–44.

Rice, D.W. (1998). Marine mammals of the world: systematics and distribution. Special Publication No. 4, the Society for Marine Mammology.

Rice, D.W., and Wolman, A.A. (1982). Whale census in the Gulf of Alaska, June to August, 1980. *Reports to the International Whaling Commission*, 32: 491–498.

Robins, J.P. (1960). Age studies on the female humpback whale in East Australian waters. *Australian Journal of Marine and Freshwater Research*, 11: 1–13.

Rosenbaum, H.C. et al. (1997). First description of a humpback whale wintering ground in Bale d'Antongil, Madagascar. *Conservation Biology*, 11: 312.

Rubenstein, Steve (2007). 22 Years Later Humphrey the Humpback Still Speaks. *San Francisco Chronicle*, 17 May 2007.

Salden, D.R. (1989) Apparent Feeding by a Sub-Adult Humpback Whale off Maui, Hawaii. *Eighth Biennial Conference on the Biology of Marine Mammals*, Pacific Grove, CA.

Salden, D.R., Herman, L.M., Yamaguchi, M., and Sato, F. (1999). Multiple visits of individual humpback whales between the Hawaiian and Japanese winter grounds. *Canadian Journal of Zoology*, 77: 504–508.

Saxon, Tim (2004). Sea Tiger, Oahu, Hawaii, last sourced on 28 September 2007 at http://www.timsaxon.co.uk

Sharpe, F.A. and Dill, L.M. (1997). The behaviour of Pacific herring schools in response to artificial humpback whale bubbles. *Canadian Journal of Zoology*, 75: 725–730.

Sharpe, F.A. (2001). Social foraging of the Southeast Alaskan humpback whale. Ph.D. dissertation, Simon Fraser University. Burnaby B.C. 129pp. last sourced on 15 April 2008 at: http://www.alaskawhale foundation.org/research/feeding&community/socialforaging&com munity.html

Silber, G.K. (1986). The relationship of social vocalizations to surface behaviour and aggression in the Hawaiian humpback whale. *Canadian Journal of Zoology*, 64: 2075–2080.

Silvers, L., Salden, D.R., Atkinson, S., Iwasa, M., Cambellas, C. (1997). A Large Placenta encountered in the Hawaiian winter grounds of the humpback whale. *Marine Mammal Science*, 13: 711–716.

Smith, T.D., Allen, J., Clapham, P.J., Hammond, P.S., Katona, S., Larsen, F., Lien, J., Mattila, D., Palsboll, P.J., Sigurjonsson, J., Stevich, P.T., and Oien, N. (1999). An ocean-basin-wide mark-recapture sturdy of the North Atlantic humpback whale. *Marine Mammal Science* 15, 1–32.

Spitz, S.S. and Herman, L.M. (2000). Measuring sizes of humpback whales by underwater videogrammetry. *Marine Mammal Science*, 16: 664–676.

Stafford-Deitsch, J. (1988). *Shark: A Photographer's Story*. Sierra Club Books, San Francisco.

Steiger, G.H., J. Calambokidis, J.M. Straley, L.M. Herman, S. Cerchio, D.R. Salden, J. Urbán-R, J.K. Jacobsen, O. von Ziegesar, K.C. Balcomb, C.M. Gabriele, M.E. Dahlheim, S. Uchida, J.K.B. Ford, P. Ladrón de Guevara-P, M. Yamaguchi, and J. Barlow (2008). Geographic variation in killer whale attacks on humpback whales in the North Pacific: implications for predation pressure. *Endangered Species Research*, 4: 247–256.

Stimpert A.K., Wiley, D.N., Au, W.W.L., Johnson, M.P., Arsenault, R. (2007). Megapclicks: acoustic click trains and buzzes produced during nighttime foraging of humpback whales. *Biology Letters*, 3 (5): 467–470

Straley, J.M., Gabriele, C.M., and Baker, C.S. (1994). Annual reproduction by individually identified humpback whales in Alaskan waters. *Marine Mammal Science* 10: 87–92.

Stubbs, H.A. and P. Colla (1996). Documented evidence and observations of a newborn grey whale calf near Point Lobos, California (unpublished), last sourced on 16 April 2008 at: http://www.hwrf.org/publications.html

Symons, H.W. and Weston, R.D. (1958). Studies on the humpback whale in the Bellingshausen Sea. *Norsk Hvalfangst-Tidende* 2: 53–81.

Tomilin, A.G. (1967). *Mammals of the USSR and adjacent countries, Vol IX: Cetecea.* (O. Ronen, Trans.). Jerusalem, Israel: Israeli Program for Scientific Translations.

Turnullo, R. and N. Black (2002). Predation Behaviour of Transient Killer Whales in Monterey Bay, California. Summary research report of talk presented at Fourth International Orca Symposium in France September 2002, last sourced on 5 May 2008 at: http://www.montereybaywhalewatch.com/Features/KillerWhalePredation0210.htm

Tyack, P. (1981). Interactions between singing Hawaiian humpback whales and conspecifics nearby. *Behavioural Ecology and Sociobiology* 8: 105–116.

Tyack, P. and Whitehead, H. (1983). Male competition in large groups of wintering humpback whales. *Behaviour*, 83: 132–154.

Urban, J.R., and Aguayo, A.L. (1987). Spatial and seasonal distribution of the humpback whale in the Mexican Pacific. *Marine Mammal Science*, 3: 333–344.

Voss, G.L. and Pearcy, W.G. (1990). Deep-water octopods of the Northeastern Pacific. *Proceedings of the California Academy of Sciences*, 47: 47–94.

Wada, S. (1972). *The ninth memorandum on the stock assessment of whales in the North Pacific.* Unpublished report submitted to the Scientific Committee, International Whaling Commission.

Walker, M.M., Kirschvink, J.L., Ahmed, G., Dizon, A.E. (1992). Evidence that fin whales respond to the geomagnetic field during migration. *Journal of Experimental Biology*, 171: 67–78.

Watkins, W.A., and Schevill, W.E. (1979). Aerial observation of feeding behaviour in four baleen whales: *Eubalaena glacialis, Balaenoptera borealis, Megaptera novaeangliae,* and *Balaenoptera physalus. Journal of Mammalogy* 60: 155–163.

Weinrich, Schilling and Belt (1992). Evidence for acquisition of a novel feeding behavior: Lobtailing in Humpback Whales. *Animal Behaviour*, 44: 1059–1072.

Whitehead, H., and Moore, M.J. (1982). Distribution and movements of West Indian humpback whales in winter. *Canadian Journal of Zoology*, 60: 2203–2211.

Winn, H.E., Bischoff, W.L., & Taruski, A.G. (1973). Cytological sexing of cetacea. *Marine Biology*, 23: 343–346.

Winn, H.E., Edel, R.K., and Taruski, A.G. (1975). Populations estimate of the humpback whale in the West Indies by visual and acoustic techniques. *Journal of Fisheries Research Board, Canada*, 32: 499–506.

Winn, H.E., Thompson, T.J., Cummings, W.C., Hain, J., Hudnall, J. Hays, H., and Steiner, W.W. (1981). Song of the humpback whale – population comparisons. *Behavioural Ecology and Sociobiology*, 8: 41–46.

Winn, H.E. and Winn, L.K. (1978). The song of the humpback whale in the West Indies. *Marine Biology*, 47: 97–114.

Winn, L.K. and H.E. Winn (1985). *Wings of the Sea*. University Press of New England for University of Rhode Island. Hanover and London.

Wolman, A.A. (1978). Humpback whale. In D. Haley (Ed.), *Marine Mammal of the Eastern North Pacific and Arctic Waters*. Seattle, WA: Pacific Search Press.

Zoidis, A., Smultea, M.A., Frankel, A.S., Hopkins, J.L., Day, A., McFarland, A.S., Whitt, A.D., Fertl, D. (2008). Vocalizations produced by humpback whale calves recorded in Hawaii. *Journal of the Acoustic Society of America*, 123 (3): 1737–1746.

INDEX TO NOTES

Adriatic Sea 141

Aetiocetes 135

Alaska 139, 149, 151, 155, 159, 160, 162, 167, 169, 170, 173–175, 177, 178

Alaska, Gulf of 152, 163

Alaska Whale Research Foundation 168

Aleutian Islands 139, 162, 173

Alexander Archipelago 167, 171

Ali'i 147

Amchitka Islands 173

Antarctic 141, 142, 149, 163

Arabian Sea 142, 178

archaeocetes 133, 134

Arctic 149, 179

artiodactyls 133,

Atka mackerel 173

Atlantic Ocean 139–141, 150, 158, 160, 163, 167, 173, 178

Australia 142, 143, 158, 173

Baja California 175

Bahamas 140

Bahia Sal Rei 140

Baie d'Antongil 142

Baker, C. Scott 170

baleen 134, 135

Balena 148

Baltic Sea 141

barnacles 136, 154, 177

Basilosaurus 134

Basque whaling 179

bathymetry 150

bats 165

Beaufort Sea 139

Bering Sea 162, 173

Bermuda 158

Big Mama 169, 170

blowhole 135,

blubber 134, 135, 137

Blue Planet 180

blue whale 134, 136, 137, 165, 166

Boa Vista 140

'boing' sound 165

Bonin Islands 174

Borowski, Georg Heinrich 137

Boston University 172

Bothnia, Gulf of 141

bowhead whale 166, 167

Brazil 141

Brisson, Mathurin Jacques 137

British Columbia 162, 169, 175, 180

British Isles 140, 141

California 163, 174, 175, 177

California, Gulf of 165, 175

Canada 139, 162, 175, 180

212

capelin 173
Cape Verde Islands 140, 158
Caribbean 139, 140
Chatham Strait 170
collisions 177
Cook, Captain James 147, 148
cookie-cutter sharks 177
Cook Islands 142
Corfu 141
Costa Rica 141, 163
County Cork 141
Cousteau, Jacques-Yves 165

Dalhousie University 143
Darling, Jim 156
Delaware 140
DNA analysis 155
Dolphin Institute, The 147
dolphins 164, 178
Dolphin, William 172
Dominican Republic 140
dorsal fin 133
Drake Bay 163
dura mater 164
D'Vincent, Cynthia 167

eagle ray 181
Earth's magnetic field 164
East China Sea 174
echolocation 134, 164–166
entanglement 178, 180
Equator 148
evolution of whales 133–136

Fabricius, Otto 138
false killer whales 152, 177
Farallon Islands 162
fin whale 165

Gabon 142
Georges Bank 140
Glacier Bay 161, 167

Gloucester Harbour 172
Gray, John Edward 138
grey whale 160, 163
great white shark 135
Greece 141
Greenland 140
Gulf Stream 140

ha 147
Hanser, Sean 168–170
harbour seals 176
Hawaii 139, 147–150, 152, 153, 155, 157,
    159–162, 170, 174, 175, 179, 181
  Big Island 148, 150
  folklore 147
  oral history 147, 148
  petroglyphs 147
  temples 148
Hayes, Herbert 172
Herman, Louis 147, 149
herring 140, 167–171, 173, 174
Holmes, Martha 180
Homer 156
Humboldt Current 163
humpback whale
  bachelor groups 152, 156
  baleen 166, 179
  birth 137, 140, 154, 155, 160, 161
  blow 147
  blowhole 174
  blubber 137, 151, 179
  breaching 1, 143, 144, 146, 155, 169, 178,
    181
  breeding sites 145, 147, 153, 179
  broadside display 153
  bubble cloud 171, 172
  bubblenet 168–171, 173
  bubble streams 159
  bull 154, 159, 180
  calves 139, 149–154, 159–163, 170, 173,
    177, 178, 180
  chin slap 145, 181

communication 144–146, 168
competitive groups 153, 157, 159
cooperative feeding 144, 152, 159, 168–173
courtship 144, 150, 152, 155, 162
crucifix block 146
distribution 139–143
dominance behaviour 153
dorsal fin 136, 174
ear 136
echelon feeding 172
evolution 136
exhalations 153
eye 136, 146
feeding 166–174
feeding call 168, 169
feeding sites 145, 146, 149, 151–153, 156,
    158, 161, 162, 173, 175
fighting 151, 153–155, 157
fishing calls 159
flick feeding 171
flipper (fin) slapping 146, 155
genitals 137
gestation 137, 160
head lunges 153, 155
helping behaviour 154
high vertical rise 172
joiners 158
juveniles 149, 154
lateral lunge 172
lobtailing 142, 145
longevity 137
lunge feeding 170
lunging 142, 143, 145, 146, 151, 153, 167
manoeuvrability 146
mating 152–155, 160, 162, 179
milk 161
migration 136, 139–142, 156, 162–166,
    173–176
nomenclature 137, 138
nursery sites 161, 178
parasites 144, 177
pectoral fin hydrodynamics 138, 139

pectoral fins 136–138, 145, 146, 154, 169,
    171, 172, 180
peduncle throw 145
penis 154
playback experiments 159
populations 139–143, 180
predators 176, 177
primary escort 153–157, 181
reproduction 160–162
secondary escort 153, 154
sex ratio 155
sexual maturity 160
singers 155–158
size 136
sleeping 174
social sounds 159
song 140, 155–159, 168
spyhopping 142, 145, 172
stranding 179
sub-adults 154
tail flukes 136, 145, 161, 171, 177
temperature control 138
throat pleats 136, 151, 166, 169, 177
tubercles 136, 138
vertical lunge feeding 172, 173
weaning 161
yearlings 149, 161
Humpback Whale National Marine Sanctuary
    179

Iceland 140
ichthyosaurs 135
Ilio Point 150
Indian Ocean 142, 158
infrasounds (low frequency) 159, 164
Ingebrigtsen, Morten Andreas 167
Inishvickillane Island 156
Intersea Foundation 167
Ionian Sea 141
Ireland 141, 156
Isabel, Isla 175

Japan 139, 148, 157, 174, 175, 180
Juransz, Charles and Virginia 2, 167

Kaho'olawe 148, 150
Kamaiki Point 149
Kamchatka 139, 162
Kanaloa 147
Kauai 162
keratin 166
Ketchikan 174, 176
Kewalo Basin Marine Research Laboratory
    147, 170
killer whale 145, 152, 169, 176, 177, 180
Kogane Senior High School 136
kohola 147
Koholalele 148
krill 140, 167, 170–173

Laau Point 150
Laeonakohola 148
Lahaina 148, 160
lampreys 177
Lana'i 150, 151
lek 156
Lefkada 141
lei palaoa 147
Lynn Canal 173

McGregor Point 149
mackerel 140, 151, 173
Madagascar 142
magnetite 164
Maine, Gulf of 140
Maku 147
Marías, Islas 175
Maryland 140
Maui 150, 151, 161, 162
Mediterranean Sea 141
megalodon 135
Meganisi 141
Megaptera miocaena 136
Melville, Herman 155

Mexico 139, 157, 174, 175, 177, 180
Minister's Son 173
minke whale 165
Moby Dick 155
Molokai 150
Mordiera Bay 140
mysticetes 134

Nantucket 148
National Marine Laboratory 180
Navidad Bank 140, 150
Nearchus 178
Netherlands, the 141
New Bedford 148
New Caledonia 142
New England 177
New York 140
New Zealand 142
Nicklin, Flip 180
NOAA 179
noise pollution 159
northern right whales 178
North Sea 141
Northwest Passage 139
Norway 140
Nova Scotia 140

Oahu 163
odontocetes 134
orca *see* killer whale
Oregon 163, 175
Oregon State University 162, 175
Okthotsk, Sea of 139

Pacific chub mackerel 151
Pacific Ocean 139, 147–151, 158, 160–163,
    167, 173–177, 180
Pacific saury 173
Pacific Wildlife Foundation 156
Pakistan 178
palaoa 147
Palaoa Hill 147

Panama 178
paralytic shellfish poisoning 177
Peloponnes 141
Penguin Bank 150, 151, 163
photo-identification 140, 141, 151, 175, 180
phytoplankton 167
pilot whales 177
pollack 173
porpoises 178
Port na bPúcaí 156
Puerto Rico 140

Queen Charlotte Islands 162

Revillagigedo Archipelago 175
right whale 167, 178
rorquals 166
Russia 162, 180
Ryukyu Islands 174

Sal 140
Salden, Dan 151, 181
Samaná, Bay of 140
Samoa 142
sand eel 140
sand lance 172, 173
San Francisco 162
satellite tracking 162, 175
Scoones, Peter 180
Seattle 180
sharks 135, 144
Sharpe, Fred 168
Shippensberg University 172
Silver Bank 139, 143, 144, 150
Sirens, The 156
Sitka Sound 162, 173
Slinky 173
Socorro Island 175
South America 141, 163

Southern Ocean 163, 173
South Sandwich Islands 141
sperm whale 147–149, 160
SPLASH 139, 180
squid 152
Steller's sea lion 176
Stellwagen Bank 140
Syria 141

Taiwan 139
tapeworms 177
Tenakee Inlet 174
tiger sharks 152, 177
Tolo, Bay of 141
Tonga 142
Trade Winds 150
tuna 164

USA 140, 179

Valdés, Gonzalo 178
Valpuri 141
Vancouver Island 175
Venezuela 140
Virginia 140
vocal mimicry 157

Washington (State) 163, 174, 175
Weddell Sea 141
West Africa 141, 142
West Coast Whale Research Foundations *see*
    Pacific Wildlife Foundation
West Indies 140, 143, 144, 150, 158
Whale Bay 174
whale lice 177
whale-watching 145, 146, 154, 160, 181
whaling 142, 148, 149, 151, 160, 177–179
Whitehead, Hal 143